About the Author

Steve Scott was born on a tough council estate in Gosport, Hampshire, in 1958 and this is where he spent the first part of his younger life. With his family, he had three-year spells in both Gibraltar and Malta, his father being in the Ministry of Defence. He eventually moved to Plymouth in 1970 where he completed his education and began his career in retailing. With his wife, Jennie, he moved to South Africa in 1982, initially on a 3 year contract with a major South African retailer. Because they enjoyed the climate and the lifestyle they decided to stay on an extra 2 years but the call of 'home' beckoned and they returned to Plymouth in 1987. Steve resumed his career in retailing, concentrating on logistics this time, a job that he initially loved and was passionate about.

His depression first started in his late teens, with the depressive periods being few and far between initially, but were to grow more frequent and longer as the years went by. So much so, that eventually he lived constantly in the shadows of Churchill's 'Black Dog'. These times were a bitter and constant battle to retain his sanity and had an immense impact on his relationships both at home and at work. He eventually succumbed to a complete breakdown in 2006 and was no longer able to work. After nearly two and half years of rest and recuperation he was able to train as a personal and business coach and is now practising these skills helping others to overcome their challenges.

The book was written just after his breakdown and the process helped him to come to terms with many dark demons and bad memories and he hopes that others reading this book will be inspired to work on their demons and memories and leave the Inside and rejoin those on the Outside.

Steve still lives in Plymouth with his family.

Foreword

The Shorter Oxford Dictionary definition of depression is:
1. The action of pressing down, or fact of being pressed down. The action of lowering or process of sinking, the condition of being lowered.
2. A depressed formation on a surface, a low place.
3. A lowering of quality, vigour or amount; the state of being lowered.
4. Reduction to a lower degree or power.
5. Dejection.

You will notice that aside from No 5, Dejection, there is no direct mention of depression being a state of mental illness but the definitions, whilst referring to other meanings for the word, could equally apply to how a depressive could feel. Dejection, on the other hand is defined as:
1. The action of casting down, the fact of being cast down.
2. Casting down, abasement, humiliation.
3. Depression of spirits, dejected condition.
4. Lowering of force or strength.
5. That which is dejected.

I suspect that those of you who are reading this book who have or have had depression will resonate with these definitions of both depression and dejection but in no way do they adequately or accurately describe how you feel, think or behave.

I must admit to being surprised at the lack of a clear definition for the mental state of depression but, at the same time, not surprised in that to each person with depression it will mean something completely different, a state that defies proper and meaningful definition in something as bland and inhuman as a dictionary.

My intention in compiling this book is to share with you my own

Insiders : Outsiders

Personal Journeys Through Depression from Both Sides of the Divide

By Steve Scott

Pen Press

First published in Great Britain by Pen Press
an Imprint of Indepenpress Publishing Ltd
25 Eastern Place
Brighton
BN2 1GJ

ISBN 978-1-907172-20-5

Printed and bound in the UK

A catalogue record of this book is available from
the British Library

Cover design Jacqueline Abromeit

personal experiences of depression, how it has affected me and the people I share the world with. I have also included accounts from other people, people who are not rich or famous but are very special and unique who have either been affected by depression themselves – the insiders, or have lived and cared for people with depression – the outsiders.

There are many books available on the subject of depression: reference books, medical books, self-help books and books documenting personal journeys through depression, usually by well known public figures. The accounts in this book are deeply personal to the contributors and they have shown great courage and enlightenment by sharing their experiences of painful times with a wider audience. Writing my own account proved to be an extremely cathartic exercise in the ongoing personal management of my severe clinical depression and has become an effective self-developmental process in ending the struggle and dancing with life.

This book is unusual in that I have attempted to combine accounts of what it is like to live with depression and what it is like for those that live and care for depression sufferers. You will discover that there are many facets to depression and each contributor has their own unique experiences and stories to tell. It is hoped that those of you who read this book who have or have had depression, will gain a greater insight and understanding of the impact on those around you, particularly those who are closest to you, and the anguish and the pain they go through as they watch you in your dark days. It is also my wish that those of you who are the carers will learn more about the inner feelings, thoughts and emotions of those who walk alongside the black dog. For those readers who have never yet experienced depression, either as a sufferer or a carer, you will hopefully take away an insight to help you better understand a condition that is so common yet so misunderstood.

None of the words in this book, however, can really be a substitute for the actual experience each person affected by depression goes through, either the cared for or the carer. They will hopefully inspire you to alter your perspectives on the illness and make you think and behave differently in a way that can support and encourage the goal of lessening the power of depression and to bring light and laughter to those dark days when all seems lost.

The power of love, understanding and positive belief is unlimited and we must strive to maximise their potential so that it may negate the power of anger, frustration and dark thoughts. Believe it is so and it will be realised, seek and you shall find.

This is not the first start in my journey through life; this started with the onset of my depression some 30 years ago, but it is the start of my understanding that my depression is a gift to me in order that I may help others in a similar place. A gift, I hear you say. Yes, the moment I realised it as so it changed my perspective completely and I have now embraced it and believe it to be my destiny and this has given me my true purpose in life. How many people can say they truly know what they were put on this earth for? It is better to embrace your foes than to fight them for you shall find a friend that can teach you many things about yourself you otherwise would not have found. Use this friend to take you to a higher level of understanding, enlightenment and empowerment. I am doing so and I am now starting the second journey through my life, one in which there will be no insiders and no outsiders.

Acknowledgements

With love and special thanks to my wife, Jennie, and children, Beau, Adam and Rikki.

Thanks also to Lyn, Grace, Alan and John for their friendship during the darkest days.

A special mention for Lucy, our West Highland Terrier, who has been my constant companion for the last 18 months and who gives unconditional love and affection.

Special thanks and extreme admiration for the contributors to the book who have allowed you into their world unconditionally. They have shown remarkable courage.

Contents

Chapter 1

Steve's Story:
Becoming a Different Person

I have severe clinical depression!

There was a time when I was unable to bring myself to use the word 'depression', either for my own use or to use it to describe what I was feeling to others. The very mention of the word would cause me to shrink with fear and self-loathing. What will people think of me? I would always wonder. That I was weak, mad, unusual, different or just putting it on? Why did I think like this?

The reasons for this are many and varied but, upon reflection, the main reason was that I was scared to admit to myself that I was not in control. I have always prided myself on being in control, a compassionate yet effective leader, a stable if overly serious person, one who sought the tacit approval of others but liked and sought his own company. How could such a person exist if there was no control over how they thought, felt and behaved? If I couldn't exist, therefore, I was useless, no-one would love me, approve of me, not least myself; and if there was no self-love how could I love others?

My non-existence became a dark void, which in turn became a place of comfort from which I rarely ventured. This became the norm; I had taught myself that it was better to be in this place and my thoughts, feelings and behaviours reinforced this view to the point that this became my world and mine alone.

This world of mine was special to me and no-one else was allowed in, just in case they discovered the real me, a depressed person. I became adept at convincing others that all was well in my world, or so I thought. I kept teaching myself new tricks to avoid unnecessary contact with the outsiders, those that would not understand; how could they, they are 'normal', they are happy, laugh and enjoy themselves. They cannot see what is happening to me on the inside.

Where did my depression come from?

Why me?

What had I done to deserve this?

How could I have avoided getting depression?

These are just some of the questions that have bothered and perplexed me ever since I felt something was wrong and with more intensity once my condition was diagnosed in July 2000. I am still wondering today as I write this book, but at least now things are getting clearer and my view on how I perceive the depression within me has changed for the better.

I was born in Gosport, Hampshire on 12th February 1958 and spent my early childhood years in Gosport, travelling with my family to Gibraltar and Malta where my father was stationed during his service with the Ministry of Defence. Eventually we ended up in Plymouth, Devon in 1970. My overriding memory of this early relocation was an incident whereby my three sisters were playing with two other girl friends on a grassy knoll, yards from our home. I was with them when a group of lads approached and started verbally abusing my sisters and the other girls. When I intervened to put an end to the abuse, I was set upon by the largest of the group and pinned down by the others, spread-eagled, while he stuffed freshly mown grass down my throat.

At 12 years old, this was a terrifying experience, choking on the grass in the knowledge that you are unable to move either your arms or your legs to defend yourself. I was distraught with fear that they may inflict further injury or insult upon me, I felt totally helpless and an overwhelming sense of being alone, despite the fact that the girls were still there but completely unable to assist. I was no stranger to fighting, being brought up on a tough council estate in Gosport, and had been involved in gang fights when I was younger, but I had never experienced such an ordeal as this before.

Although the assault only lasted a few minutes it seemed like forever. When was it going to end? When would they leave me alone? But end it did and although physically I was unharmed, mentally it left a scar on me that wasn't to become apparent for many years.

When I was 17, another event occurred that I believe has been significant, not only at the time, but also in my development from a teenager to an adult, and was to have a major role in forming my personality, values and beliefs for years to come. For the first time my parents had consented that I could go camping in north Cornwall with my two best friends on our own. This was a very exciting time; I had been vested with trust and responsibility by my, at times, over-protective parents and this was a real opportunity to step into the adult world for the first time.

We were dropped off at the camp site and said our respective goodbyes to our parents and we three eager teenagers, soon to be grown-ups, hastily assembled our tent and went about exploring our surroundings with total freedom. Everything went well at first but after a few days tension arose between my two friends and I, which ultimately led to a complete breakdown in our relationship, culminating in a fight between them and me. Today, I am still unsure about the cause of the tension or the fight and I suspect I have deliberately or unconsciously erased this memory from my consciousness. No amount of recall, hypnosis or therapy has been able to retrieve the reason or reasons and, in any case, the fact that the fall-out occurred is irrefutable and unchangeable, whatever the cause.

The end result was that my two friends threw me out of the tent and told me I was no longer welcome. What was I to do? I considered phoning my parents to come and get me but rejected this based on the fact that I had been given special licence to go on this holiday without them and my pride wouldn't let me admit to them that I wasn't capable or responsible to be on my own. I was also scared to confess to them that I had had a fight with my friends and fallen out with them in such an unsavoury way.

My only option was to sleep rough for the rest of the week and await my time until we were due to be picked up at the end of the week. This too was a daunting prospect; I had no suitable equipment or clothing to sleep rough other than my sleeping bag. I had some money but not enough to feed me adequately for the rest of the week; all the food I needed was back in the tent with them. Despairingly, I chose the latter option and decided to rough it out in the elements and on my own.

The remainder of the week was spent trying to look after myself as best I could and in reflecting on what had happened to me and us. How could the relationship with my two closest friends have ended like this and so suddenly? What would I do now? If this could happen between best mates, why bother having friends at all? It was at this point, alone and feeling hurt and isolated, that I resolved to never allow anyone else to get close to me again. I figured that if I took this approach then I would never get hurt again. From then on, I would be totally self-sufficient; I could give myself everything I needed, such as trust, friendship, respect and commitment. Self-reliance was the key to future survival. The barrier went up and it was I who decided who could come inside and I would decide both when and where. I took control of the barrier, I became a gate-keeper and I only made fleeting forays to the outside, the other world, but I was careful when I crossed the line lest I became vulnerable, rejected or hurt. In any case, it was so easy to cross back into my world on the inside. From this point on I was to become a different person.

Looking back now, was this the time of my life that depression started? Was this the trauma, plus the previous incident, the trigger that shaped my life to come? It is said that depression can be caused by trauma and the meaning you attach to it. It is also said that it is not the event in itself that causes the problem but it is how you experience the event that is significant. Is this what happened to me? Certainly, my reaction to the falling out and the permanent loss of my closest friends – we never saw each other again – was possibly extreme and I did attach significant meaning to the situation, leading to a long-lasting change in my personality and character.

I became withdrawn, almost reclusive, serious, and created a self-imposed limitation on the number and type of relationships I had. I never allowed anyone else to create a relationship with me; it was always me who gave permission for it to happen. I rarely went out, preferring to stay in my bedroom and listen to my music, shunning attempts by others to join in social gatherings. Why did I need to have the company of others; they would only hurt me. I was totally self-reliant and independent. I didn't need others for my world to feel complete.

Unbeknown to me at the time, I was teaching myself new habits, new beliefs and new values, and the longer this situation went on, the stronger these neural pathways were becoming. I looked for ways to strengthen my views, I saw other people occasionally fall out or I heard other people speaking ill of their friends behind their backs, and these reinforced my position that I was right. I ignored the fact that generally friends had a great time, could be relied upon, trusted and had meaningful and respectful relationships. I was becoming to experience the world as I wanted to see it rather than as it really was.

After a period of time, I found I was losing the art of socialising and losing the skills to be able to effectively communicate with others, particularly in group situations. I was afraid to say anything in case this led to a confrontation, someone might take offence at what I had said and this could possibly lead to a fight and/or further rejection. Instead, when I did go out, I kept quiet and stayed in the background on my side of the barrier. This was becoming a successful tactic; I no longer fell out with people I knew (I no longer referred to them as friends – friends hurt you). The more this worked the harder and longer I used this tactic to cope. I even started to develop tactics to avoid meeting people I knew or I left early without telling anyone I was going. I excelled at creating the illusion to others that I was in the crowd and enjoying myself with them, but really I was mentally by myself. These successes provided more reinforcement that this new way of living was working.

It came to the point that I relished the opportunities to be by myself as much as possible. I still went out with people I knew at the weekends to nightclubs and pubs but I was always by myself, in my own world, doing what I wanted to do, where I wanted to be and when. My skill at disguising my true feelings was getting better with each week that passed. Then suddenly, out of the blue, I met a girl who totally mesmerised me. She was a school friend of one of my sisters and she arranged for us to meet one evening at a night club. Whilst I was desperate to meet her I was also scared; I would have to step outside my barrier and be with her on the outside. I felt intimidated, vulnerable and ill at ease. It was a long time since I had had any meaningful relationship with a girl. I didn't really know how to act, behave or even engage in small talk. Our arranged meeting was a real ordeal for us both and it was my fault. I was clumsy, tongue-tied and out of step with my surroundings. She, on the other hand, was very confident and relaxed initially but I could tell that it was all going wrong. As the evening wore on she spent more and more time going off talking and dancing with her friends.

Despite this, there was something about her that drew me to her, perhaps it was that she was what I had secretly wanted to be, in terms of confidence, self-esteem, and relaxed in the company of others. Subconsciously, I was jealous of this but at the same time I knew that this was not my world. But I wanted her and this presented a real dilemma for me, which in the end was taken out of my hands when she told my sister that, whilst she liked me, she didn't want to have a relationship with me; I was too quiet and reserved.

I was devastated by the news and again felt the pangs of rejection and retired back to the safety of my bedroom where I brooded over the disappointment for several weeks. Looking back, I wonder now whether this was a period of depression, my first that I can recall. Again, I reflected on the experience and again rejection reinforced my view that when you cross the barrier to the outside you become vulnerable. This was not going to happen again, I must stay on my side at all costs.

But the heart is a powerful force in the body and I happened to meet the girl again, quite unexpectedly, and this time I was more relaxed and confident, I was after all on my side of the barrier. If there was to be a relationship it would be on my terms. We hit it off this time and started seeing each other regularly, which was brilliant, but I was still cautious and on my side. I really liked her and we did have some fun together. However, over the next few years our relationship became an on/off affair, with any endings emanating from her. There was an occasion when we had arranged to meet and at the last minute she cancelled, citing too much school work to do. I still went out and, low and behold, I saw her out with another bloke. What a kick in the teeth!!

That was it. I decided I would never let her back into my life again. But every time she beckoned, I ran back. What hold did she have over me? She was truly a confident woman who decided what she wanted and went out and got it, including me. It took me over 30 years to realise that she had the power and control in the relationship and I had surrendered my personal power to her. This was a very revealing insight and it was a pattern I was to repeat many times in future years.

Eventually, I could no longer take the repeated hurt, anguish and soul-searching I went through each time she ended the relationship so I took the initiative and decided to leave her for good. I resolved that enough was enough and that it was best to retreat to my side of the barrier again. I became a recluse again, barely venturing out, rejecting most appeals by people I knew to go out with them. My own company again became preferable and self-reliance was the key to my survival.

Chapter 2

Descent into the Black Hole

I eventually met the lovely and gorgeous Jennie at a local disco-theque in May 1979. We married several years later and she has shared my life for the last 28 years, in all its ups and downs. In all those years I have suffered depression to a lesser or greater degree, with periods sometimes lasting a few days, a few weeks and constantly since 2000. As my life evolved the times that I have become very depressed occurred more and more frequently and lasted longer and longer. Looking back, these depression spells were usually brought on by an argument, a disagreement, pressure at work or by a nightmare, of which I will speak more about later.

Despite having a loving and caring wife, I still tended to be an intensely private person, rarely sharing my inner thoughts, feelings and emotions. These I kept locked away behind my barrier; they were mine and no-one else was entitled to know what they were. I did, however, spend more and more time on the outside but all the while I knew I could retreat back to the inside whenever I wanted to avoid conflict and disagreements; these, remember, lead to confrontations and rejection.

I managed to build a successful career in management, which involved running teams of people as many as 150 strong, but I always shied away from dealing with large groups, preferring instead to delegate these tasks to a small group of trusted managers and supervisors. I was still afraid of groups, I was afraid of making a fool of myself, worried about saying the wrong thing and afraid of acting inappropriately, as these could again lead to situations which would leave me vulnerable, exposed and subject to rejection.

This fear of rejection was so strong I wanted everyone to like me and, at times, there were consequences to this that actually placed demands on me that were difficult to manage. Dilemmas became a constant companion during my earlier management years, particularly when I was directly responsible for disciplining staff and still wanting them to like me. If I didn't discipline them my managers and supervisors would not respect me nor would the rest of the staff. Discipline them I did, but I would worry about the hearing for days ahead of the event, it would occupy my mind constantly, I would rehearse and replay how I would handle the situation over and over again. There was much angst and regret after the event even though I tried to convince myself that what I was doing was right.

All through this, my expertise at disguising my true feelings of low confidence and self-esteem worked well. People saw me as confident, composed and decisive and my career continued to go from strength to strength. This imposed two pressures upon me. The first was my burning desire to earn more money with which to support my family and provide them with better things in life. The second exposed me to more and more difficult situations and pressures at work that were often at odds with my desire to be liked and accepted by everyone.

I started working longer hours to faithfully and efficiently carry out my duties as assigned to me and, in addition, I sought to be creative and inventive to support the need to be accepted. This became a double-edged sword in that the harder I worked the more responsibility I was being given. I was slowly getting out of my depth from a mental health perspective and depression started to really bite, although at the time I never knew this, I was too busy to notice. I attributed these times of sadness, lethargy and numbness to the fact that I was tired and working too hard. There are times when I can remember myself shut in my office close to tears for no apparent reason, paralysed by dark thoughts of death and suicide, self-doubting inner talk that destroyed my self-esteem and a crisis of confidence. My barrier still worked effectively for me and I was able to appear 'normal' for everyone else to see. Deep down I was being eaten away slowly by my depression, but worse was to follow.

At home during these periods of depression I became very difficult to live with. I was angry, argumentative and distant and took out my frustrations on my wife and children. I flared up at the slightest thing and used my weapons of silence and withdrawal increasingly; in effect I retreated behind my barrier, sometimes for weeks and even months at a time. These times were extremely difficult for Jennie as she never knew where she stood, what it was that had angered me or what I was thinking. I would not and could not communicate with her. I was a man, a successful manager and I could cope, I didn't need help as I would deal with any issues on my own. I had to have my independence; if I didn't she would see me as less than a man and would lose respect for me and may reject me. I couldn't cope with further rejection, just thinking about the possibility of that happening was extremely painful and stirred those traumatic thoughts of past rejections.

Eventually these periods of depression would, usually quite suddenly and for no apparent reason, lift and I would return to 'normal'. Naively I then expected the whole world to forgive me and forget how bad a person I had been and if I was okay then they too should be okay. To her enduring credit, Jennie forgave me and was probably relieved to have her old Steve back. I had no thought of what I was doing to her mentally. After all, I was working long hours, earning a decent salary and occupied a senior position in a relatively large organisation. What else did she need?

Everything I was doing was for my family and my own personal reputation and acceptance.

Years later I was shocked and deeply dismayed to learn of the effects my periods of depression were having on Jennie, but I will let her tell her own story later in this book.

By now my depression was arriving more regularly and staying longer; weeks rolled into months until in November 2000 it arrived suddenly and has stayed with me until now. I say suddenly not as a literal expression but as a reality. I distinctly remember a night when Jennie had gone out with some friends for a drink and I went to bed early. As I was attempting to get to sleep I felt the depression arrive as a wave of despair slowly washing over me, from the top of my head and down through my body. I find it truly difficult to accurately describe the experience but the nearest thing I can liken it to is being possessed by an evil force, a dark cloud descending over me and through me, shutting out all the light. It was a real and physical experience that I was consciously aware of and filled me with dread and foreboding. I had experienced sensations like this before when depression arrived but never with such intensity. On the other hand, I also knew when depression was leaving as I had felt a lifting sensation, almost as if the light was being let in, the opening of curtains so to speak. But this was different, very different.

That night was a bad night for me. I was restless and drifted in and out of sleep, experiencing nightmares of such intensity that they were almost hallucinatory. I was bathed in sweat, cold and clammy, a steady trickle of dampness all over my body.

In the morning, it was as though the sun had never risen. Deep, dark and seemingly impenetrable clouds seemed to hover above my head. I had no energy at all and just wanted to stay in bed; but I had to get up, I had a job to go to. I couldn't go sick – what would people think of me? I was indispensable and I needed to support my family. The fact that I was entitled to go sick and go on sick leave never entered my head, it was never an option or a choice. My pride would not allow me to take time off. Who would do my job if I was not there? Who would ensure that my team would complete their tasks? I wrongly considered myself essential to the role my team played in the overall function of the department. Quite simply, I put the job before my health. My mind and body was screaming at me to stop and to take a rest but I knew best. I could cope, I had had depression before, it would pass and I would get better. My work would take my mind off my depression, or so I thought.

Although I have previously referred to these times as depression, I still did not know that this was what it was. I wasn't to realise this for another two years.

During these dark early days Jennie endured a living hell, not knowing whether she had done anything wrong or was supposed to have done something but had not. I just did not communicate with her. I had retreated behind my barrier and, despite numerous attempts to find out what was wrong with me, I was steadfastly unwilling to share my innermost thoughts and emotions with her. After all, I was the man in the house, I needed to be strong and masculine, and men cannot be seen to be weak and vulnerable. As far as I was concerned, I was just feeling down, in a bad mood and under pressure. If I let her know these things she would not respect me, might even reject me, so it was better to keep these things to myself.

Eventually, she started leaving on my desk articles on stress and depression from newspapers and magazines for me to read. At first, I just dismissed these as illnesses and weaknesses other people got or have. Not me. I was independent, self-sufficient and reliable, completely above falling prey to stress or depression. But as my depression stayed and the symptoms got worse and worse, I started taking notice of these articles and started doing my own research into what depression was and how it affected people. To my surprise and horror, I realised that I ticked most of the boxes: I had no interest in life, no sense of humour, low libido, poor sleep, I had put on weight, increased my alcohol intake and, to some extent, dependency. My aversion to social contact became stronger and stronger and I eagerly sought my own company in as many situations as possible. Most of all, I felt as if I was in a deep, dark and slimy hole with no hope of climbing up the sides. If I looked up, all I could see was dark clouds and so there was no incentive to climb out anyway. Nothing, but nothing, cheered me up. I was completely morose and sullen all the damn time.

Although this should have been a breakthrough in realisation of the dire situation I was in, it actually deepened the dark state of despair I was feeling. I was overcome by guilt, shame, sadness and anger at the thought I could have succumbed to the dreaded depression. Why me, I thought. What had I done to deserve this? I had tried to be a good person, husband and father. I felt an immense sense of guilt that it had been Jennie that had spotted what was wrong with me and that I had been treating her so badly all these years. I felt sad for myself; I wallowed in self-pity and felt ashamed because others would see me as weak and as a failure. I became angry with myself and the rest of the world, for the same reasons as I felt guilty, sad and ashamed. How could I have so many differing emotions about the same thing? The more I thought about the illness, me, my thoughts and feelings, and about others, the more I became confused, and the harder it was to think straight and accept the position I was in.

I had extreme difficulty in coming to terms with the reality and my whole life became consumed with my thoughts, from waking up to going to bed; all I could think about was depression. The more immersed in my own world I became the more I excluded those around me who cared for me and who could have helped me at this lonely time. But I had a burning desire to try and deal with this by myself; after all, I had conditioned myself over the years to do exactly this. What could anyone possibly do or say that could help? It was me stuck in the dark hole and they had no idea what it was like or what I was going through. What made it worse was the stigma attached to depression. I had heard colleagues at work casting disparaging words at others who had gone sick with depression. What would they say about me?

It is very difficult to precisely describe how I felt at this point; it was as though my world had ended rather than the beginning of a new chapter, which is how I should have felt once I knew I had depression. You can tell people what depression means to you but unless you actually experience it they will never really appreciate the effect it has on you and how you live your life.

Eventually, and after much angst, I decided to see my doctor and it was with a heavy heart and much trepidation that I made the appointment. On the day I was due to see the doctor I actually considered cancelling; after all you often get better once you've made the appointment, don't you? Well, I didn't and sat in front of him and described how I had been feeling and for how long. I felt like a child as I sat in the chair, as a schoolboy sat in front of his teacher trying to explain why he hadn't done his homework, with the feeling that my excuse wouldn't be accepted. I expected him to say that I should pull myself together and get a grip, that it was all in my mind and other people were worse off than me. To my utter surprise, he was very sympathetic and understanding and made me feel at ease talking about my depression. This was a huge relief and I even managed to return to my adult state as I took in the details of depression that he explained, how it affects people, how it could have come about and the types of treatment available.

He prescribed Prozac, which I had heard about on television and read about in newspapers, and whilst I had some reservations about taking drugs, I decided that this would be better than the alternative of doing nothing. He asked me about my job and the levels of pressure involved and, not wanting to go sick, I lied about the type of job I was doing, my responsibilities and stress levels. I really did not want to go on sick leave; I reasoned it would have been better to continue working, firstly because of the stigma and secondly because of my own self-esteem. Little did I know that this was undoubtedly the worst decision of my entire life, past and present, but more of this later. You have to deal with the facts you have available to you at that moment and the level, or lack, of experience you have with the subject matter. The doctor reluctantly agreed that I should continue staying in work but that I should monitor how I was feeling and what effect Prozac was going to have on me.

Although I felt relieved that I had now talked to someone about how I was feeling, I was also concerned that my medical records would now reflect the fact that I had depression and what this would mean in the future for my career and for things such as life insurance, mortgages, etc. So it was with mixed feelings that I left the surgery to collect the Prozac from the pharmacy.

The next big hurdle to cross was to discuss the appointment with the doctor with Jennie. I had deliberately failed to tell her that I had made the appointment; perhaps I had hoped that the doctor would have said I was okay. Anyway, I resolved to broach the subject and be honest with her and to face the challenge head on. This would mean leaving the safety of my barrier and laying myself bare, sharing my secrets and innermost thoughts. At an opportune time when

14

the two of us were alone, I told her that I had seen the doctor and he had diagnosed depression. She immediately broke down at the news and we both shed copious amounts of tears, although for different reasons.

She felt relieved that it was an illness rather than me, or her for that matter, that had been causing my behaviour and she was sad for me. I, on the other hand, cried because I was guilty and ashamed of the way I had been treating her and also because I was overcome with self-pity. Upon reflection, this was a defining point in my challenge with depression; I had lifted the lid on my world and, to some extent, this changed our relationship for the better.

We discussed depression and me at length and Jennie seized the opportunity to tell me things she had kept bottled up for years, and this was an extremely cathartic experience for her. For me, hearing these things from Jennie was equally enlightening and frightening. I had never truly realised what she had been going through, I had been too busy looking inwards that I had virtually ignored her, not from a husband's perspective in providing an income and caring for the children, but from a lover's and friend's perspective in that I denied her love, compassion, sensitivity, conversation and, most of all, intimacy. At times, we had gone months without making love or even having a cuddle and this had created doubts as to her sexuality, womanhood and attractiveness.

I was full of admiration for her, that she had persevered with me and had not rejected me – my greatest fear – and I counted myself lucky and fortunate to have such a stoic, brave and caring wife. Even today, I am amazed that she stuck with me and continued to be my friend, partner and lover, despite the depression continuing and at times getting worse.

We decided not to let the children know I had depression; there was no point in them worrying unduly and we hoped that the Prozac would provide the necessary relief from the symptoms. Jennie did, however, want to share the news of my depression with her closest family members, I think to help explain my anti-social behaviour towards them and my sullen behaviour generally.

For my part, I shared the news with three of my closest colleagues at work, which I considered a risk, but it was also an attempt to elicit help and understanding. The reaction I received was mixed; they were indeed understanding but, with the exception of one, they generally felt awkward and uncomfortable discussing it with me. It felt that they didn't know what to say or suggest, almost as if they were avoiding it at times, scared to ask how I was in case I said I was not feeling too good. I don't blame them. What could they say or do? How many times do you come across someone with depression? They had no prior experience of this and, therefore, they had no skill at dealing with a depressive. I liken this to not knowing what to say to a colleague who has lost a loved one; nothing can console them, you cannot say everything will be okay because it will not be. They are grieving and only they feel the hurt.

Although only a few select people knew I suffered from depression, I felt vulnerable and had a sense of being watched by others, to see how I was behaving and to see what my mood was. I also felt what seemed to me their pity, although in all likelihood it was just sympathy. The vulnerability affected my self-esteem and confidence; in the company of those who knew I became a child again rather than an adult with an illness. After all, I would not have felt like a child had I broken an arm or a leg and had a plaster cast, so why should I feel like this with depression? I guess it is because depression is invisible; there is virtually no tangible evidence of the pain or the hurt you are going through; it is deep within you and over the years I had learnt to deceive people about how I really felt. Generally, people we did tell were shocked to hear the news, which in a way paid a perverse tribute to my disguise and deception.

This regression to a childlike state created its own demons for me, which compounded the mixed feelings I was going through. I was still coming to terms with the diagnosis, the reality of discussing this with Jennie, my own internal dialogues and sharing my illness with others. Dealing with this additional challenge became a real burden and I constantly questioned my own sanity and sense of being. I just could not understand why I felt like a child in the company of adults. I was conscious of my size; I felt small, insignificant and immature. Gone was my self-perceived confidence and assuredness or were they just illusions anyway, part of my disguise and deceit? Were they ever there anyway? Perhaps I had spent so long on the inside of my barrier that I had come to deceive myself all along? Had spending all my time in my world contributed or been the sole reason for my depression, or was there something else?

Whatever the reason, I continued to take Prozac and go to work, attempting to live as normal a life as possible. But what was 'normal'? Surely 'normal' was not depression, there had to be a better way and a better life, but I really did not have the skill or knowledge to become 'normal'. True, things at home became better now that Jennie was coming to terms with me and understanding my condition, but work continued apace, even to the point that I was promoted several times and my workload increased proportionately. On the one hand, this satisfied my enduring need to provide and support the lifestyle I wanted my family to have, but on the other hand this exposure to ever greater challenges and responsibilities was gnawing away at my mental health.

Chapter 3

Living in the Black Hole

One day, out of sheer desperation at being right down in the deepest, darkest part of the pit, I decided that I could no longer cope with this illness by myself and resolved to enlist the support of a counsellor. This is when I met Alan, who was to become my counsellor, mentor and eventually close friend and role model. I rang a number of counsellors from the Yellow Pages and talked to several of them, describing my needs and how I felt at that moment. After talking with Alan I knew immediately that this was a kind, compassionate man who I could trust. Over the years I had developed an intuition that allowed me to know whom I could or could not trust. Alan fell into the former and I made an appointment to see him the next day.

Seeing a counsellor felt like admitting defeat, that despite all my confidence in my own abilities and that I could only trust myself, I recognised that I needed professional help. I had to see someone to talk to, someone to share my fears and anxieties with, my feelings of utter despair and loneliness. Alan did not disappoint me. I felt immediately at ease with him and once I started to talk, the floodgates opened and I spewed out my whole story, almost without catching breath. What a relief it was to be able to disgorge all this stuff I had kept bottled up for all these years. It was like releasing a valve on a pump that was about to burst. I am not ashamed to admit that this was a very emotional session for me and it was a good job that Alan had a plentiful supply of tissues to hand.

It was especially a relief to be able to openly discuss my depression with a person who did not judge me in any way; he offered me no pity or sympathy, only empathy and understanding. I did not go to see a counsellor for pity or sympathy, I was giving this to myself in abundance anyway. What I did go for was sharing and support, which I received aplenty. In addition, Alan provided me with a refuge, a safe haven where I could go once a week and discuss how my week had been and what I might do constructively between each session. My visits to Alan became an essential ingredient in my life, which at the time I was living day by day. Alan had this wonderful ability to mix empathy with humour, metaphor and total understanding. I felt safe in his capable hands, I had trust in his abilities and guidance and, above all, he was there to help me unconditionally. He demanded nothing in return, save for his fee obviously; he did not want to be my emotional crutch, he merely wanted me to get better. Over time, this is what happened. He guided and facilitated a process whereby I was able to take more control over my thoughts, feelings and overall mood. He gave me a belief that I could and was getting better. After nearly 12 months we started to run out of things to talk about and this he saw as a sign that real progress was being made. I have never come across a businessman who was so glad to lose a client before but I shall never forget the smile on Alan's face when he declared that, in his opinion, I did not need any further therapy or counselling. I agreed readily but I actually felt disappointed that our relationship had come to an end, or so I thought.

Unfortunately, it was circumstances rather than any lack of skill on Alan's behalf that led me to start seeing him again after a 12-month sabbatical. To this day I can unequivocally say that Alan has provided me with many of the tools in my tool box and has been, and still is, a very influential figure in my journey of recovery and I will be indebted to him for the rest of my life.

My new management position brought me into contact with the higher echelons at work and, in particular, with George (not his real name), whom I had known and worked with for over 20 years. During these years we had enjoyed a see-saw relationship of ups and downs, good times and bad but never unmanageable. In the early days we played both 5-a-side and 11-a-side football together and he was a very capable administrator with excellent business acumen. Now, however, our relationship became strained as he and I faced increased pressure for results and this was exacerbated by our different styles of leadership and management. He was an autocrat who thought he was a democratic manager but was extremely negative most of the time, more interested in 'who' than 'why' or 'how' when things went wrong. I, on the other hand, had a democratic and participative style that encouraged initiative and responsibility, which he viewed as soft and weak. At times he was a bully who shouted, stamped his feet and thumped the table with displeasure; and then, when the moment had passed, expected everyone to like him and respect him when he bought coffee or a pint.

Due to my sensitive nature, I invariably soaked up his negativity unconsciously, assuming that this was mine and not his. Other colleagues I worked with also exuded negativity and I was very receptive to this and allowed it to affect my general outlook and mood. My boss and I soon had a tumultuous relationship with conflict and disagreement becoming the norm. I started to dread going to work, never knowing how he might be, what faults, real or imagined, he would find and how he would react.

I started to smoke again, having given up for nearly 12 years, and every morning I used to go to Plymouth Hoe at 6.30am to spend some time looking at the sea and to have a cigarette, working up the courage to go to work. I clearly remember this time as the time when thoughts of suicide came into my head; how easy it would be to jump off the cliff and crash myself onto the rocks below and fall into the sea and drown. What a relief this would be – no more depression, no more work, no more responsibilities – a release from my prison. Although these thoughts were there, there was no serious intent but I did become extremely ambivalent towards my own mortality. What if I smoked and got cancer; I was thinking of killing myself anyway, what was the difference? Cigarettes became my friend. I could go out and have a smoke at work if things got difficult or hectic or too much. They calmed me down, gave me comfort, and were an excuse to have some time by myself.

These times on the Hoe were precious to me. They became the calm before the storm. I could not face the day without them. They became a comfort blanket but they were not reality. Work was reality and inevitable. The walk from the car park to the office became drudgery and got harder and harder to do. I started going out for lunch, which quickly became a liquid variety, to escape the confines of my office and to create an illusion of temporary respite from the demands of my work and my boss. Having a drink at lunchtime became a habit and one drink was becoming two. I justified that this way was the way to cope though in truth it was a false reality and a dangerous path to take, but I was oblivious to this in my depressed state. I was looking for sanctuary in a physical or three-dimensional state, not knowing that sanctuary lies within.

Smoking was a pleasurable experience and relief for me but I was ashamed that I had taken it up again after so long. I dare not admit that I was smoking to my family, they so disapproved of the habit and, naturally, they would be concerned about my health. So I had another secret to keep from them, yet more deceit and disguise. I would stop smoking mid-afternoon in order to rid myself of the smell of tobacco by the time I got home and then hope they would not notice. But as my dependency grew, the more risks I took, smoking later and later in the day, until I became so bold as to stop on the Hoe for a cigarette on the way home and then suck mints in the forlorn attempt to dispel the aroma.

How naïve I was to imagine that one can smoke and hope that no-one will notice. But what did I care; after all I was unconcerned about my health. I had suicidal thoughts, so what if they found out that I smoked! The constant denial and lies about smoking were wearing me down and adding to my lack of self-esteem, best if I came out and told them the truth, whatever the cost. At least this would be one burden less to carry around and worry about.

How selfish I was to risk my health and not to think of the impact this would have on those who loved me. When the fact that I smoked did eventually come out, my family, and in particular my daughter, were devastated. Their disapproval was instant and uncompromising but it did not deter me from smoking. My needs, I reasoned illogically, were greater than theirs. How arrogant and selfish I had become. Their concern did bother me and as time wore on and the more I smoked the more I became disgusted with myself. Smoking in itself thus became a source of fresh inner turmoil, created endless internal dialogues of self-loathing and thoughts about my own needs and the needs and concerns of my family. The more I mulled this over the more I reached for the cigarettes and needed the high the nicotine was giving me. The very reason I had taken up smoking in the first place, to relieve the symptoms of stress and depression, had now become a reason for stress and depression. As I write my account I am still smoking, still being wracked by the pleasure versus pain dichotomy, yet I am convinced that one day I will rid myself of the habit and one of the fuels that the fires of depression are feeding on.

Whilst there are certain aspects of my behaviour I consider to be selfish, there are other aspects that compelled me to help others, sometimes at the expense of my own health. I had throughout the years seemed to revel in the role of the rescuer, a knight in shining armour riding to rescue the damsel in distress. I frequently responded to the needs of others, such as family members, strangers, colleagues at work and even the job itself with a selflessness that verged on the impressive but wholly irresponsible. Whilst in my rescuer mode, I neglected my own needs, indeed I was probably unaware they existed anyway. The focus was on rescuing, helping and healing others. While there are a few people who are truly able to sustain this completely altruistic lifestyle, the vast majority have needs that lie beneath the surface which are unmet and often unseen. In these cases, and mine, it was a motivation to help others that became an extension of a deep desire to heal a wounded part of themselves and myself and I was starving for the kind of love and attention I was giving out to those around me.

. For many reasons, I was unable to give myself the love and attention I needed and so I gave it to others. This did not mean that I was not meant to be helping others, but it did mean that I would do well to turn some of that energy within. One problem with the rescuer model was that I got stuck in this role, always living in crisis mode at the expense of my inner peace and personal growth. Because I was unable to resolve my own inner dramas, I played them out in my relationships with others, drawn to those who needed help and most often unable to acknowledge my own needs or get them met. In the worst cases I enabled the other person's dilemma by not knowing when to stop playing the rescuer and allowing them to figure it out on their own, denying them the opportunity to grow and develop. I also denied myself the strength to turn within and face the needy aspects of my own psyche and empower myself to become a true source of self-healing.

In the end, it was me that suffered inner burnout from overgiving. I had an inability to admit to having needs of my own and I became unwilling to be vulnerable. Help would only come when I could admit to myself that I needed it, by acknowledging my humanity and my real pain. It was many years before this acknowledgement came and I would realise that if I were to help myself I would have to inspire others to help themselves. This has become a significant part of my journey through the darkness and out of the pit of depression.

In the meantime, my condition worsened. It became harder and harder to function at all, let alone keep going at work and at home. My early morning trips to the Hoe became more frequent, to the point that I went there every day before work for a cigarette and to steel myself for the day ahead. My office had no windows or natural light and heightened my feeling of being in the prison of depression. There were days when I cocooned myself in this office, door locked, at times weeping uncontrollably and hoping that no-one would knock on the door. I would just sit and stare at my work, my mail and my computer with hundreds of e-mails, utterly confused about what I should do first, generally ending up doing nothing or just dealing with trivia like rearranging my office or desk.

My relationship with others, and particularly with my boss, deteriorated as I kept myself to myself and avoided all unnecessary contact. I constantly battled with my boss, whose negativity just fuelled my own despondency and made my condition worse. I desperately tried to ensure that I still performed as best as I could; my pride and my perfectionism would not allow me to do anything else, but at times this was an impossible task. This, though, became another reason to beat myself with my stick as I contemplated the fruits of my labour and realised they had not met the unrealistic standards I had always set for myself. As far as others were concerned, it appeared that I was still in control, fulfilling my responsibilities as always, but deep down I was really disappointed with myself, frustrated and angry. Time and time again, I was driven by the unachievable standards I demanded of myself. The fact that I was the main breadwinner and provider for the family ment I could not let them down. I was driven by my concerns about how others would see me otherwise they might reject me, or think less of me. My reputation as a calm, thorough and caring manager was more important at that time, and before, than my own health and wellbeing.

It became a vicious circle, spiralling dangerously downward, with a certain inevitability that I failed to recognise. The worse my depression became the harder I tried to hide it; the more work was pushed my way, the harder I tried to complete it; the more time I spent at work, the more I battled to keep the lid on a box of explosives. Little did I realise that the fuse had been lit a long time ago and had been burning slowly but surely and I was close to imploding.

I had been project managing the implementation of a new computer system, which as with most projects, had had some difficulties, particularly with the integration of the new software with the existing software. George called a crisis meeting two weeks before going 'live' and whilst everyone else was confident of success, I was not and I alone voiced my concern. At this point, I was experiencing two completely different emotions; I just wanted to break down and cry and, on the other hand, I was extremely angry and, probably confrontational. George became very aggressive with me when I told him that a delay in implementation was required. He raised his voice, went red in the face and tried to bully me into changing my mind. I reacted strongly to this approach and stood my ground, not knowing whether to fight or flee. He made my mind up for me by dismissing the others in the meeting and demanding to see me in his office "right away!". I told him that I had said what needed saying and would say no more. I stormed out, dumped my folders in my office and promptly left the building to have a cigarette.

When I got outside the building, I just walked and walked, barely able to control myself and my emotions. I was confused, angry and tearful at the same time. What was I to do now? I ended up on the Hoe without knowing how I had got there, had a coffee and numerous cigarettes whilst all the while my internal discourse was running riot. I thought to myself that now was the time to end it all; I could jump off the cliffs and into the water or onto the rocks below and I would be free forever from my job, my boss, my depression and the prison I had created for myself. No more dark clouds, black dogs, deep pits and iron bars. I stood on the cliffs looking down for what seemed hours, incessant chatter running through my mind, crying uncontrollably as I thought of my family and the love they had for me. Surely I could carry on for their sake, but what about me and my needs? I had fought the fight but I had lost. I couldn't go on with this life anymore, I'd had enough of suffering.

My confused stupor was brought to a sudden end when a work colleague spotted me and approached. I could not jump now he was there, I still had my damned reputation to consider after all. Funny, I thought, one minute I was prepared to kill myself and the next I was more worried about what he thought of me. I'm sure psychotherapists reading this will have a field day trying to explain this. Undoubtedly, this unintentional intervention probably saved my life and in a very large way was responsible for continuing suffering and despair but in another way ensured that I kept on fighting. I went back to work.

Chapter 4

The First Breakdown

I avoided George for the rest of the day and left early. When I got home I went straight to my bedroom and broke down, weeping tears of sadness, shame and sorrow. I hadn't committed suicide but I couldn't go on either. I just did not know what to do, I was completely lost and bereft of any sensible thoughts. I felt cast adrift in rough seas in a boat that was slowly sinking without a bucket or the inclination to save myself. This was the lowest moment of my life so far; how much further would I sink, how much longer could I go on? I had lost the will, the resolve and the stomach to continue fighting the black dog. He had won! I had lost! That was all there was to it.

Jennie came up to see me, suspecting that all was not well. She had become adept at judging my mood just by looking at me. When she came in the room I just fell into her arms, seeking comfort as a child does with his mother when he has been found after being lost. I cried and cried and cried, so much so that I could not even tell her what was wrong, the tears drowning out the words. Confusion reigned again as I felt both ashamed at myself for being in such a state and humiliated for allowing it to have got this far. A real man does not cry!

Eventually, I was able to tell her about my day, although I omitted to tell her about my suicidal thoughts – some things are best left unsaid. She was visibly upset at seeing me in this state but was warm and comforting, a real rock of compassion, reason and strength. We talked for a long time that evening, which helped me to gather my thoughts somewhat but I still reasoned that to go back to work tomorrow was the best thing. She argued long and hard against this; she could see no sense in continuing with the stress and strains of my job, and significantly with George. Go sick, she implored. No-one will think less of you, she said, but I had other ideas. My earlier shame and sorrow had turned to anger. I'd show him that I would not back down and let him win. It had become a personal duel, me against him, and even with depression, I was not going to let him win, no way!

Next morning, I was back on the Hoe, smoking my cigarette as usual, reflecting on the events of the previous day. With equal measures of trepidation and assertiveness I went into work to face the music. Some time later that morning George called me into his office. Here we go, I thought, this is either going to end with him sacking me or me resigning, I could see no other way out. He was stubborn and arrogant and I was determined to face up to the challenge and stick to my values and principles. However, upon entering the office he informed me that Jennie had phoned him and told him about my depression and the state I had been in the previous evening. He wanted to know what he could do to help, particularly with my workload. Confusion reigned again. I was initially angry with Jennie for divulging my secret of the depression, how it was affecting me and for going behind my back. She had no right to do this, I was the decision-maker about me. I was a man, other people should not know how I felt, it would leave me vulnerable and impotent, especially to a man I did not respect or care for. I was confused also by my boss's apparent change of heart and display of compassion and understanding. What should I say, how much should I say? How much could I trust him? What if he did not respect the confidentiality of what I was going to tell him?

I decided to tell him that yes I did have depression but, in order to preserve what I thought was my dignity and pride, I did not reveal the full extent of my condition. After a brief discussion, he agreed to look at my portfolio of responsibilities and to take away some of the more mundane tasks and allocate them to someone else. I left the office not knowing whether he was genuinely concerned for my welfare or whether he was acting merely to obligate his responsibilities as an employer. I had previously heard him, and others, talking derogatively about current and former employees who had gone long-term sick with mental health problems and so my concerns were well founded. These feelings of doubt were to remain with me for the rest of my time with this employer.

Not long after this my employer and I began talks with a larger sister organisation who were looking to take over certain functions of my responsibilities and they were looking for people with my skills to work on a national project. Great, I thought, here was an opportunity to leave a negative and overly political environment in which I was working, the prison cell of an office, and to start afresh. In my severely depressed state I reckoned that I could leave the depression behind; after all the grass is greener on the other side and I was breaking the manacles of stress and overload. The new job involved working on a project where I had a limited number of people to deal with, I would have no direct reports to look after and my boss would be miles away in the Midlands. The job would entail a certain amount of travel and staying away, which Jennie and I had discussed and agreed that this was not a bad thing. It would give us some space to reflect and consider our relationship and, hopefully, make it stronger.

After some months, I duly transferred to my new employer and began work on the project. I was extremely relieved to leave my old employer and the bad memories that went with it. My old boss even eulogised about me in his farewell speech on the day I left, but at the back of my mind I still believed that he was less than congruent, but I smiled through gritted teeth and let him get the applause.

For the first six months, my depression did indeed get better. I was enjoying my new role and liked the company of my new colleagues who, whilst they worked very hard, knew how to enjoy themselves, and included me as much as I would let them. My barriers were still up and I did not admit to any of them about my depression. The slate was clean and I was hardly likely to make it dirty unnecessarily. Initially, staying away from home two or three nights per week was enjoyable; I liked the space to be able to reflect on what had been happening in my life and what I had to look forward to.

However, the constant travelling and staying away became a poisoned chalice. In my first 12 months in the job I had driven 55,000 miles, more than four times the national average. The amount of time I was spending away from home had increased to the point where I was now staying in a hotel for four nights of every week, having been assigned to a project in east London. My depression was slowly getting worse and it was beginning to affect my relationships both at home and at work. So much so that Jennie eventually had had enough and one weekend she asked me to leave. Whilst I knew that I was an extremely difficult person to live with at times, it still came as a complete shock and surprise to me that it had gone this far. I was absolutely devastated. My depression had made me selfish and inward thinking and although I knew my behaviour was unacceptable, I believed I was unable to change it. Depression ruled supreme.

Jennie explained that she could no longer deal with me, she was constantly walking on egg shells when around me, afraid to say the wrong thing and upset me. In the past when we had argued or disagreed, I used passive aggression to get back at her. Sometimes these periods would last for months. The atmosphere in the house was palpable, although we did our best to disguise it from the children. I would only speak when it was necessary and we essentially lived separate lives with no intimate moments between us, not even a kiss. I often displayed great anger and frustration over the smallest thing, especially if things did not go my way. I was a perfectionist, everything had to be done perfectly each and every time, regardless of the importance of the task, and this would upset Jennie.

Because I shunned and avoided unnecessary contact with other people generally, I had become an embarrassment to Jennie as I was sullen, unfriendly and unwelcoming to her friends and family. This was not because I disliked them or I was deliberately rude to them, it was just the way I was. I really did not want to engage with them – they might want to speak to me, ask me questions or worse still want something from me. I even behaved this way to my own family, so I was not being selective, it was just that my family did not live in Plymouth and I only saw them rarely so it was less obvious. I just felt safer behind my barrier; it was my comfort zone and it was where I felt safe, even though I knew deep down that it was wrong to be there. I had been doing this for so long now that it was now natural for me to be behind the barrier. I had taught myself new beliefs and habits and, on the face of it, these were serving me well.

Once you become known to behave a certain way, you cannot change or else others will notice and comment on this change and you hate people talking about or to you, particularly about personal matters. You want to be unnoticed, invisible, and almost irrelevant. You want to be left alone to get on with your life, doing things your way; you know what is best for you. They do not have depression, they do not understand. How could they? They are not in that dark, slimy pit with you, they are not followed around by that black dog. They have not been so low that you become ambivalent about death, to the point that you could easily just end it all by your own hand. I just wanted to be left alone!

I went back to work in London on the Monday morning and during the five-hour drive I could think of nothing else but the fact that I had been asked to leave the marital home and my three children. Once again, complete confusion reigned. I was incapable of thinking through things rationally or even making a decision. The whole gamut of emotions surfaced, receded, resurfaced over and over again. At times I could hardly drive due to the tears in my eyes, running down my cheeks and my nose streaming. What an absolute wreck. Then anger – real anger, desperate anger. My speed increased the angrier I became. Who cared if I had a crash on the motorway at high speed – certainly not Jennie, she had asked me to leave. It would even be convenient for both her and me if I crashed and died! This anger would be followed by frustration. Why could I not get better? Why did I have to have depression? Why me, what had I done to deserve this? How could I get better? How could I change this for the better so Jennie would have me back? Then I would wallow in self-pity, which would only serve to bring back the tears and the feelings of despair, loneliness, hopelessness and rejection. Poor, poor me.

How I got to work I am not sure, I hardly remember the journey at all, the landmarks I had passed or the time it had taken. I went to my office and closed the door. I did not want anyone to see me nor did I want to see anyone lest they noticed the way I was feeling or the way I looked. I could not function properly anyway and the last thing on my mind was work. I avoided contact as much as possible for the rest of the day and left early to go to my hotel and cocoon myself in my room to be left alone with my thoughts and my depression.

I phoned Jennie in the evening but it was a very emotional and tense conversation that we had. We did chat about the events of the weekend but the actual details of the talk we had are unclear now. I guess I was too upset to remember. In any event, nothing was resolved.

The rest of the week was a blur; all I can remember was that I did my best to complete my work on the project despite the pains of depression, which were getting more and more severe. Others noticed my sombre mood and a few even asked if I was okay but I dismissed them by saying that I was "a bit under the weather". Usually in the evening those employees who were staying in the hotel would meet up for a meal and a few pints and I would have joined them, but now I preferred to stay in my room, ordering room service instead.

Sleep, always a trial, was now even more difficult with so many conflicting and confusing thoughts running around my head, like a merry-go-round out of control. I got beyond the point of being tired, the restless leg syndrome (or Akathisia, a side-effect of the anti-depressant) was rampant, so much so that I had to keep getting up and walking around my cell of a hotel room. I would frequently get dressed and go outside to have cigarettes, a tactic that had worked before, but without success. Sleep became a holy grail for me but the more I became frustrated about it the less I was able to drop off. Some nights I would get no sleep at all and eventually I would just give up and go to work to see if concentrating on my work would take my mind off things at home.

After what seemed an eternity, the week came to an end and I left for home at midday on Friday to miss the rush-hour traffic on the notorious M25 and west-bound M4, which was unusual as I would normally leave in the early evening. During the drive I could prepare myself for a difficult and challenging weekend with Jennie. I had to get a resolution somehow. I had to know where I stood, where I was going to go and what Jennie wanted for the future. Despite the opportunity to clear my mind in the five-hour journey and arrive at conclusions for myself about what I wanted for the future, decisions as always were hard to come by. A plethora of choices, options and possibilities clouded my judgement and, I reasoned, Jennie would be making the decisions anyway so why bother. Just accept that what will be will be!! Easy said, but hard done. Somewhere deep down there is a personality within me that has its own needs, desires and wants but I was afraid to connect with it and bring it out in case this created a conflict situation and, worse still, real rejection.

Even in this time of criticality, I decided to subdue my inner-self and subjugate myself to the circumstances. Looking back on this now, I wonder at why I was so cowardly in the face of such a crisis, but hindsight is a wonderful thing, and nonetheless I have difficulty respecting myself for lying down and giving up. I arrived home mentally and physically exhausted. I had no will or even compunction to resolve the issues with Jennie. As usual, Jennie welcomed me home with love and compassion but I felt the welcome was tinged with slight trepidation and foreboding. She had become extremely adept at recognising my mood just by looking at me and I just knew she knew how I was feeling. I knew also that she was not looking forward to the weekend. Typically of me, I steadfastly refused to discuss anything that night, reaching for the bottle of wine instead to escape my responsibilities. I made all sorts of excuses not to talk about the situation, which understandably made Jennie angry and frustrated. I guess she too had been doing some real soul searching during the week and needed to release her pent-up anxieties and to do it soon.

Selfish as ever, I refused to listen or talk and drank even more. How stupid was I? It would have been in my interests as well to talk the issues through but no, I had to hide behind an alcoholic glaze. Eventually, at Jennie's persistence, we did talk the next day and she aired her true feelings, thoughts and concerns at how my depression was affecting her and our relationship. She was prepared to give our marriage another go but I had to behave better towards her and to make every effort to battle my illness. She did love me but didn't like what I had become and was really worried about me, afraid of what I might do to myself and although she knew about depression and had tried to understand it, she couldn't help me if I did not let her in to help.

The fact that she had said that I could stay was a huge relief and gave me hope. I tried to explain to her how I felt but I still was economical with the truth; no point in worrying her unnecessarily. I watered down the facts of how I had been coping generally, what it was like being away from home stuck in hotels not sleeping. I tried to convince her that I would get better, it was just a bad time at that moment. I'm not sure at all that she really believed me, but she did her best to support me and provide the love and comfort I desperately craved.

Trying to put this behind me, I went back to London with a combination of determination to get better and of fear that I was actually teetering on the edge of a very steep cliff. The pressure of work and being away from home became greater as the weeks went by. What was surprising was that I was still able to achieve results and get things done but this was at a high price to my mental well-being. Physically I was also going downhill fast, rarely eating and drinking and smoking far too much, particularly in the evenings. Hotel rooms can be really lonely places and mine had become a virtual prison, dark and depressing.

I had an appraisal, my first with the new company, and my boss concluded that whilst some of my goals had been achieved well, others had not. This was a blow to my self-esteem and self-respect, particularly as I had not quite agreed with his outcomes and rationale. But I did not speak up or defend myself, I just sat there like a little child before a teacher, a lump in my throat and a rising anger deep within. He followed this up with some criticism of my current project, which again in my opinion was completely unjust. This served to only deepen my sense of being a naughty child again and I retreated further into my shell, unable and unwilling to stand up for myself. This was the last straw; my credibility, which I had always valued and prided myself with, was shattered and I felt sick in my stomach. There was nothing left. I had become a shadow, anonymous and insignificant, I told myself; even my boss now questioned my existence it seemed. That night my thoughts were about suicide, nothing but suicide. I was a failure at home and now at work. Nobody wants a failure and failures are worthless.

Chapter 5

The Second Breakdown

I drank too much that night, again, and sleep did not come at all. I paced the room, went out for cigarettes and raided the room's mini-bar for another drink, had more cigarettes and thought about my mortality. It was a long night, the longest I had ever known. I knew that I had reached, and more significantly, passed the Rubicon from where there was no going back. The walls of the room closed in on me, the ceiling seemed lower and the darkness was darker than normal. This was no longer my prison – it was my hell, a living hell from which there was no escape. Even death could not be this bad, could it? By the morning I was a complete wreck, emotionally washed out, my thoughts nothing but flotsam and jetsam floating around in a sea of uncertainty. It was now Thursday 4th March 2006 and the following day I had a day's holiday, so I packed my bags, took a long hard look at my room – my hell – and left, checked out and went to work.

Strangely, I arrived at work with a determined ambivalence to whether I performed well or not. I was assertive to the point of being unusually aggressive and I unconsciously went about clearing my desk, unknowingly packing all my personal belongings into my briefcase. I left at lunchtime without saying goodbye to my colleagues of the last six months, not looking back at the project I had been so involved in. It was the end but at this point it was still not intentionally so – it was unconsciously so.

I drove home in a stupor, knowing I had to do something but not knowing what. I could not carry on like this any longer. My world was at an end, I was dead inside and my senses were numb. On the spur of the moment I decided to ring Alan, my therapist from a year ago, to see if he could see me the next day. He had helped me before and perhaps he could help me now. He agreed to see me at short notice even though he was really busy. What a relief this was, at least I could talk things through with someone who was not emotionally attached to me and who would listen without judging me or without the fear of being rejected by him.

On Friday 5th Match, I met Alan at 8.30am and it all came out; it was as though he was a tap on my valve and I could let all the pressure out. Alan listened attentively and empathically, asking the odd question here and there and it was a huge relief to just talk and talk, divulging all the dark thoughts and inner beliefs. He suggested I should consider seeing my GP as well with a view to going on sick leave as, in his opinion, I would only get worse and that I was either having or would have a major breakdown. Hearing this from him was both a surprise and a breath of fresh air. He had always advocated staying in work before as this was a distraction to depression and gave a sense of normality and purpose, but here he was saying I should stop. I knew deep down he was right and there was absolutely no sense in fighting it.

Even though I was relieved to have talked this through with him and felt I now knew what I had to do, I went home and completely broke down. Luckily, no-one was at home, I lay on the sofa and cried and cried, completely uncontrollable tears of sorrow and self-pity. I had indeed reached the end, there was nowhere else to go. I assumed the foetal position, almost wishing I could crawl back into my mother's womb where it was warm and safe. I eventually dozed off and on for a few hours but each time I awoke I would immediately break down and cry so much that I no longer had any tears left. I tried to phone the doctor to make an appointment but I just could not get the words out, breaking down yet again. There was no way I was going back to work but this hurt, really hurt; what about the project – we were at a critical point – what would everyone think of me? They would think that I had abandoned them, that I could not handle the stress and pressure and this ashamed me immensely. What would my family think – I was the man in the house and I had to perform, provide and support them. But I could not; I was useless like this to anyone, let alone to myself. I was a letdown, another failure; no self-respecting person could go sick in this situation, but here I was doing just that. The more I recognised the position I was in the harder it became for me to accept, and the more I was awash with self-pity and shame.

Jennie, who had recognised my deep despair the previous evening, rang me in the morning to see how I was. I could hardly speak to her on the phone, in between the sobs and blowing of the nose. She said she would come home as soon as possible. Although I wanted her to come home I was scared to face her, scared that she would see me like this, scared that she would lose respect for me and ultimately scared that she would reject me. These were stupid thoughts; she loved me and had stood by me all these years and probably would now, but that is how I thought at the time. If I hated myself why shouldn't others hate me as well?

When she did come home, I broke down yet again, capable of only letting her cuddle me, like a little baby, while I wept over and over again. I could not speak coherently, I did not make any sense at all, I just wanted to be comforted and told every thing would be all right. My inner child was on the surface again and I had no control, just glad that Jennie was there to provide a safe pair of arms into which I could snuggle. Initially, she shed some tears as well for herself and for me, but she soon took control and phoned the doctor who promptly booked me off for two weeks.

So, the decision had been made albeit not by myself, but I did not care anyway. I was beyond caring for myself and I was just relieved that a decision had been made. I didn't care about my self-respect or my self-esteem anymore either. I really didn't care about anything other than being in Jennie's comforting arms. I spent the rest of the day in a daze, not knowing much about what was going on around me. I had turned inside, gone deep down and was oblivious to the rest of the world.

In the meantime, Jennie had arranged an appointment at the

doctors, phoned my parents (who had no idea I was suffering so badly from depression) and explained to our children for the first time that I was sick and was not going back to work. She contacted my boss and explained that I was unwell with depression and had been given two weeks' sick leave. He, apparently, showed concern for my well-being and said that he understood. While all this was going on, I felt even more ashamed and vulnerable on the one hand but relieved on the other, relieved that my secret was well and truly out and that I had at least two weeks' grace in which to gather my thoughts and to try and make sense and meaning of my current situation.

Jennie had other ideas, though, and told me that she thought I should not go back to work, at least for a very long time. My breakdown, she reasoned, was a sign that my mind and body had reached a point where it could no longer cope and needed a complete rest. Although I argued that I was needed back at work because of the criticality of the project at this point, I did so with absolutely no conviction and knew deep down she was right. There really was no alternative. I did have to take some time out, get off the roundabout of the world, so to speak, and just be a bystander for a while. The prospect of doing this was completely alien to me; all my life I had been a doer and producer rather than a witness and I had no skills or experience to carry out this role.

How does one totally stop doing things they have done all their life? I had no idea, but I did know that if I carried on my condition would only get worse, my depression would reach critical point, I would be a candidate for a stroke, or worse still, a heart attack. What a dilemma I was in but all I could do was to just accept it and try and relax. Easier said than done as my mind continuously wandered around: to work and my commitments there, especially my colleagues; to what my parents and children would think of me; to myself and my inner turmoil and conflicts; back to work and so on and so on. Thoughts of being a failure, weak, a mere mortal, even being a malingerer (I just had to pull myself together!), a basket case and even that I was mad, barking mad!

The reaction from my children was great, really mature and understanding. My daughter, who was 14 at the time, who had always been very close to me, paid me loads of attention and liberally showered me with love and affection. I had noticed in the past that when I was particularly depressed she seemed to want to cuddle and hug me and tell me she loved me more than usual, almost as if she was in tune with my feelings and could sense that I needed compassion and company. My eldest son, who was 21, was particularly distressed to see me in my state of disrepair and shed a tear or two on my behalf. He has always been a sensitive boy who deeply values family life and connections and I was really touched by his display of emotions and the strong hug he gave me, almost as if that would make me feel better. My other son, who was 18, was at university in Wales but when my wife phoned him he was his usual stoic and practical self, offering to come home straight away to be with me and take care of things around the house. Jennie declined his noble offer, reassuring him that I would be well looked after and just needed to relax and take things easy. What a great family I have!

Although my parents knew I was suffering from depression, it came as quite a shock to them to hear that I had broken down. We had previously spoken about depression in broad terms and the effect it was having on me, but in order to keep them from worrying too much – they were not in the best of health themselves – I watered down the severity of the symptoms and their effects on my well-being. I wonder now whether that was a mistake and it would have been better to have been more honest at the time and spared them the shock of the breakdown. What is done is done and I cannot change what has happened, but I still do not know if I did the right thing or not. My father, in particular, had, and still has, some difficulty understanding depression. I believe this may be due to a number of reasons. Firstly that he cannot 'see' the illness and, therefore, has no visible sign of what is wrong – that there is ostensibly no major organ failure like a bad heart, and that depression is a relatively modern diagnosis and he had little or no experience of the condition during his years as a father, employer and employee. In addition, he gave me the impression, both verbally and physically, that mental illness can be put right by grit and determination, the 'pull yourself together' and clenched fist approach. Whilst he may be right to a small extent, depression is not a set of curtains. Finally, my father always needs a reason for things to be and depression was no exception. 'Why?' was his constant question and I feel to this day he cannot quite accept what is. I have explained to him a number of times that depression can be caused by many reasons – such as trauma, stress, pressure, chemical imbalances or all or any combination of these – but this appears to be not good enough. Although I love my father dearly, it does irk me somewhat that he cannot just accept me for what I am or I have become because of depression and his needs to justify my illness with a reason.

Maybe I am being too harsh on him, on reflection, as this question of why I have depression has vexed me for years without coming to any firm conclusions, merely hypotheses. On the other hand, maybe like father like son. I had always held my father in the highest regard and readily modelled myself on him at times, and perhaps his influence was driving me to answer the very question he is seeking to answer. In my defence, however, I believe it is more important for me to find the answer to why, for my own benefit and peace of mind, than it is for him, an interested spectator. After all, what would he do with the answer anyway, nothing but satisfy an innate need to seek understanding, which in his reality serves no purpose. If it was one of my children who had become mentally ill, I would be more interested in what I could do in the here and now in order to facilitate healing and alleviate the symptoms rather than searching for the answer in the past.

It is important, however, not to labour the point; my father always means well and has constantly been there for his children no matter what and I accept that we are all different and he is entitled to his views and beliefs. This uniqueness of human beings is what makes life so special and interesting; how dull it would be if we were all the same.

Chapter 6

The Slow Climb

My going sick from work has, upon reflection, been the start of a second life for me, one in which I have started to challenge my old beliefs, values and principles as I continue with my journey to wellness. One of the first significant steps I took along this path was to visit a healer, who is a close friend of my wife's sister. This was a huge leap of faith for an avowed sceptic and complete agnostic in all things religious and spiritual. To my surprise, I found the session very stimulating, relaxing and enlightening, all at the same time. Lyn, the healer, was extremely understanding of my condition given that she has a family member who is suffering from severe depression. During the healing session, she played meditation music in the background and laid her hands on my head. It was not long before I could feel heat coming from those hands, which was very soothing and comforting. Although I attempted to meditate during the session, I found it very difficult not having tried this before but it was enough just to close my eyes, listen to nice soft music and feel 'healing hands' on my head. The other difficulty with meditating was that, as usual, there was a constant chatter of self-talk buzzing around my mind, like bees around a honey pot. No sooner did I attempt to focus on nothing then along would come a stream of thoughts, distracting my endeavour for inner silence and peace.

The session seemed to end all too quickly but I was surprised to learn that it had taken half an hour – it only felt like ten minutes. Lyn afterwards described events and people that had come to her as she was performing the healing and, incredibly, was able to accurately describe and even name my late grandfather on my father's side. Wow! I was dumbstruck at how this could be possible and decided to put aside my scepticism and just accept this information unreservedly. I did not immediately feel any distinct relief from the pains of depression but I was suitably impressed by the experience to have more sessions; there appeared to be more to this than met the eye.

I continued to see Lyn weekly for many months for healing sessions and now we meet for regular meditations where we send out collective healing to the universe. Meeting Lyn has had a major impact on me and my quest for inner peace and spirituality, the question of who I am and why I am here. Over time, I did find the healing very beneficial and helpful, particularly during the darkest days and Lyn's teaching on meditation and self-healing were really useful in between sessions. Gradually, I became better and better at meditation, I am able to quiet the mind, dismiss the idle and negative self-talk and really focus on the here and now. I even started receiving images and visions myself as well as having the sense that my late grandfather and others were with me in the room and supporting me spiritually on my journey.

Between Lyn and Alan, my therapist, they were responsible for setting me out on this quest for self-development and enlightenment, recommending numerous books to read and CDs to listen to. Without their help and direction I would have been like a rudderless ship, just drifting around searching for a lighthouse in a dark and dangerous ocean. They provided me with the will and the support to undertake this path, knowing they would be at my side to carry me should I fall or stumble along the way. Along with my wife and father, Lyn and Alan have been the two most influential people in my life and I am eternally grateful to them.

Talking of Alan, I started seeing him again regularly so that I could talk things through, explain how I felt and discuss issues that were bothering me at the time. I looked forward to these sessions; Alan has a tremendous gift of making you feel at ease in his company and his jovial manner and smiling face always brightened up my day. He is a fantastic listener and superb user of metaphor and analogy, which he used to illustrate points he was trying to make. He constantly challenged my limiting self-beliefs and negative thoughts and provoked serious debate over sensitive issues with a silk glove approach, which stimulated me to self-challenge my innermost feelings and emotions. He was, and still is, a veritable rock to me in my time of dire need and has become a role model and mentor to me in better times.

Alongside healing from Lyn and personal therapy from Alan, another significant moment in my life came in April 2006, some six weeks after going sick. Alan invited me to spend a week at a villa owned by himself and his wife, Grace, who is also a therapist/counsellor, in the mountains of Andulucia, Spain, with four other clients. The aim of the week was to engage in group and individual therapy sessions and to move blockages in self-development and inspire us to make changes in our lives that would make positive differences. Whilst I thought the week would be good for me, I was still incredibly vulnerable and reliant on my family and secure home environment. Plus, I was very withdrawn and was apprehensive at spending time with four strangers in a strange place in a foreign country, potentially laying my emotions out for public airing and scrutiny. I talked it through at length with Jennie and decided to go.

The week was superb; I immediately felt at home in 'Anam Cara', Alan and Grace's purpose-built villa surrounded by superb views of the Andulucian mountains. The other four clients all turned out to be female and, interestingly, Aquarians – not that I am too interested in star signs, but I did think it unusual if not insightful. The five of us immediately gelled and I felt unusually comfortable talking about my depression, where I had been, why I thought I was like I was and what my thoughts and beliefs were. I don't think I have been so open with so many people, especially strangers, ever before and it was an incredibly enlightening and empowering experience. The others too felt the same way and it was not long before we were all engaged in deep and meaningful discussions about our own experiences with depression and anxiety, what helped, what did not, and what we wanted for the future. With Alan and Grace's excellent guidance, we all worked through a structured plan that encouraged positive change and mutual help and support. We reviewed all the key areas of our lives and identified those areas that needed particular attention and focus, which were then addressed in group and individual sessions.

Having thought a number of weeks previous that I had dropped off the end of the world, here I was in sunny Spain making a first few tentative steps towards a new life. They may have been small shoots of positive, happy thoughts but I could start to envisage them growing into real solid oak trees. I was being open and honest about my depression to not only others but more importantly to myself, and this was a real revelation. I was also so happy during those days in Anam Cara – I had found my smile again, which I thought I had lost, I had discovered my sense of humour and above all I had re-discovered 'me'. I was just being myself for the first time in many years and it was great, bloody great!

There were times that I had to pinch myself to make sure I wasn't just dreaming and that at some point I would wake up and I would be back in my cell of depression. But it was true and I wasn't the only one feeling this way, others in the group were also having the same great time. In a way, we were all feeding off each other's elation and happiness, a collective sharing of euphoria and well-being whilst learning about ourselves in a positive, safe and public environment. For me, the week was a turning point in my fight with depression; for the first time in a very long time I had hope, hope that depression can be beaten, hope that I could make a difference in my world and hope that I could be 'normal' again. The week had given me a taste for life without depression, life with humour, happiness and laughter and life without barriers. I went home with a lighter bag than what I went with and this was progress.

When I arrived home, Jennie immediately spotted the warm glow surrounding me – no dark clouds above my head now! I was actually smiling for a change and even if she wasn't as perceptive as she was, she would have recognised a different me coming home. What a difference a week could make. I told Jennie all about my time away, leaving nothing out, which in itself was unusual in that I would normally only give out the barest of information, brevity was king as far as I was concerned. Dear Jennie had to endure an experiential outpouring like she had never endured before and must have wondered what had hit her. I didn't even give her time for questions, which was generally how she managed to extract information from me and, to her credit, she allowed me to ramble excitedly on and on.

The next few weeks were like a blur of activity. I wanted to do this, do that, read this book and read that book, go here, there and everywhere. I was on a high and enjoying every moment of this but at the back of my mind there were distant thoughts that perhaps I was really on a rollercoaster ride and at this precise moment I had reached a peak and that, just maybe, I was heading for a fall, a mighty fall. I mostly tried to dismiss these thoughts from the conscious level because when I was on a high I was always overly optimistic – nothing could go wrong again, I was out of the pit and there was no need for the barrier. Equally, however, when I was down I was always overly pessimistic – nothing could go right again and I would never break down that self-imposed barrier. Because of this optimism, I never had a contingency strategy, I never planned for the bad times and refused to learn and use the appropriate coping mechanisms to stop me falling back into that pit. Enjoy the moment, I had been told; live for now, it is the only place you can influence; and so on and so on. Good advice if you are normal or feeling good but not so if you have depression. My reality is that by living in the now, I ignored the possibility of my mood changing in a moment or overnight and, as a result, the fall always led to disappointment, frustration, vulnerability and anger.

Today, I accept the highs and am grateful for them, but I am also conscious that this can change but that this is okay, this is normal for me. Always with good comes the bad and I need to accept this without judgement or evaluation. I have been in both places now and I have developed skills to deal with these situations, skills that do not involve me being emotionally attached to how I feel, but more of this later. The point here is that I was particularly unprepared for the fall that did occur then, and it hit me very hard.

Having had the best period in my life for over five years, it was a shock when overnight my depression returned. I could feel it come back, a physical sensation of being possessed by dark thoughts, a deep and unbroken layer of cloud above my head. Fuck, I thought; those lingering, unconscious doubts had come true. Had I manifested the return of depression because of these doubts? Whatever, I thought, I was back where I used to be and, perversely, there was some comfort in being depressed again; this was where I was regularly, this was where people now expected me to be and I had again the safety of my barrier, almost as if I was back home. How bizarre was this – almost unexplainable – why should I feel at home in a depressed state having just experienced three weeks of absolute joy, happiness and normality? I guess that over the depressed years I had become accustomed to thinking and feeling as a depressed person; this had become normality for me and I had learnt the skills, thought patterns and beliefs that supported depression and rejected the invasion of skills, thoughts and beliefs that supported normal non-depressed behaviour.

Buddha said "You are what you think yourself to be" and this was certainly true for me. Others, such as Eckhart Tolle, have also said "you are not your mind". Whilst I concur with both, they are contradictory and, to me, confusing. If I am not my mind and if I am who I think I am, who the hell am I? One thing for sure is that I am a depressed person but is this a physical manifestation or a mental manifestation? It may even be a combination of the two and, as I juggle the two concepts over and over again, the more convinced I am that there really is an element of both at play. The question is, however, like the chicken and the egg conundrum, which came first?

Chapter 7

Searching and Dreaming

Grace, from Anam Cara, told me about a client of hers that had depression and that it was a symptom of a condition called Addison's Disease. This condition is caused by low levels of cortisol in the blood, which is a result of the adrenal system not producing enough. Cortisol is an extremely important hormone in the body, specifically in body growth and development and can affect the body's immune response and its ability to respond to chronic stress. Levels of cortisol, therefore, affect the body's emotional state, energy levels and its ability to respond to infections. I became interested in Addison's Disease and decided to undertake some research into the condition to see if my depression was being caused by a physiological reason. I used both the internet and the public library to seek information and to corroborate data from one source to another. This research indicated that Addison's Disease could be caused by trauma or an attack on the autoimmune system leading to damage to the endocrine system of which the adrenal gland is a part. Looking back at my past, I figured that the event with my two friends could constitute a trauma and not long after this event I contracted viral meningitis, which attacks the autoimmune system.

Were these just coincidences or were they contributory factors in my depression? Digging further, a percentage of people suffering from Addison's Disease have Vitiligo, a condition whereby pigment is lost from the exposed areas of the skin, such as face, hands and feet. I contracted vitiligo in my early 20s, losing colouration on my hands and feet, skin that never tans, it just stays white. Things were now starting to look promising but I needed more evidence. This was forthcoming as I looked closely at the list of symptoms of Addison's and I noticed that again, a percentage of people with the condition have tinnitus, which I have had since my early 20s and have suffered with ever since.

I purchased a book by an American doctor that specifically reported on adrenal fatigue, of which Addison's is part, and this confirmed my previous findings. In the book, the author suggested that the best way of finding out whether a person has adrenal fatigue or not is to have a saliva test to establish the levels of cortisol. I managed to find a private laboratory that would supply saliva kits and then analyse the samples of saliva, producing results in both written and graphical formats. This laboratory duly provided a set of test tubes into which I gave samples of saliva at set times of the day. These were sent off and returned several weeks later with my results.

I was expecting the results to come back indicating low levels of cortisol, confirming my earlier theoretical research. It was a real shock when the results revealed that rather than having low levels of cortisol, I had levels that were almost three times higher than the average! Back to the drawing board, internet and medical text books. Accordingly, it became apparent that high levels of cortisol cause Cushing's Syndrome and, whilst I had some of the symptoms of this, I was unable to tick as many boxes for this as I could for Addison's. This left me confused but not disheartened. Armed with my research and my saliva test results, I went to my GP to ask for their interpretation and to ask for a cortisol stimulation blood test. My GP was understanding but showed no interest in the results of the saliva test, indicating that this came under the realm of 'alternative medicine', which the NHS did not do. Nor did they share in the validity of my research, stating that it was inconclusive and that many people have vitiligo and tinnitus without having depression. They did, however, agree to the cortisol stimulation test. They informed me that there was very little, if any, evidence to suggest a link between Addison's or Cushing's and depression.

I left the surgery thoroughly frustrated and disappointed. It seemed to me that all the NHS wanted to do was prescribe anti-depressants, of which by now I had tried many types without any noticeable positive effect. I was pleased, however, that they had agreed to the blood test even though the American doctor and author had concerns over the veracity of the accuracy of the results. Anyway, I went ahead and had the test, which subsequently came back with the results that my cortisol levels were within the normal range. This felt like the door being slammed in my face; as far as the medical profession were concerned there was no evidence to support a physiological reason for my depression.

Disappointed but not undeterred, I then looked into the effect the thyroid gland has on depression, as the thyroid had consistently appeared in my earlier research. Sure enough, levels of chemicals produced by this gland can have an effect on depression, particularly bi-polar or manic depression. Once again, I purchased a book looking at illnesses caused by a malfunctioning thyroid system and whilst there was some evidence connecting some of my symptoms with depression, there really was not enough to wholly suspect that I had a problem with my thyroid. However, this book and others indicated that a thyroid test should be conducted when depression is first diagnosed. I, to my knowledge, had not had this test done and went back to my GP to request the test. During my discussion with them they told me that they had, in fact, carried out this test at the same time as my cortisol stimulation test and tests on my levels of certain minerals, such as sodium, magnesium, calcium, etc. All these tests showed that there were no unusual levels that gave cause for any concern; my thyroid, in particular, appeared to be functioning okay.

Another door slammed shut! Reluctantly, I had to accept the results of the tests but I am far from convinced that there is no physiological reason for my depression, either in whole or in part. Firstly, why were my saliva tests showing high levels of cortisol? Secondly, the range of levels described as 'normal' for cortisol are large – between 5 and 95 for example – and although my results fell into this bracket, my levels might not be 'normal' for me as an individual. Thirdly, if depression is not caused by physiological influences, why should I be aware of a physical sensation when depression comes and goes? Fourthly, depression is often described as being a chemical imbalance and drugs are prescribed to treat these imbalances, so what organs are producing the imbalances in the levels of chemicals? Although I have scaled back my quest for a medical explanation, I have not lost hoping in finding a solution here.

At this point it is relevant to talk about medication. Over the course of the last seven years I have been prescribed a variety of anti-depressants – from Prozac, Seroxat, Citalopram, Mirtazipane, etc, to my current Venlafaxine. With the exception of Venlafaxine I felt no perceptible benefits but rather was affected by side effects to a lesser or greater extent. The worst side effect I experienced was restless leg syndrome or Akathisia (more of this below), which was debilitating at night. Venlafaxine, apparently, is a new generation anti-depressant and has been the only drug where I have found a degree of relief from the symptoms of depression, albeit it has only taken the edge off the worst feelings. Any relief is good relief as far as I am concerned and I continue to take the drug to its maximum dosage.

My experience of the medical profession in relation to how they have treated me is mixed. The GPs I have seen have been sympathetic and relatively understanding to a point but they seem preoccupied with prescribing drugs of various types and in different dosages. It was six years before they decided to refer me to an NHS psychiatrist but they never recommended cognitive treatment (which I was paying for privately with Alan), light therapy with SAD lamps, dietary changes or psychology. By way of interest, I did invest in a SAD desk lamp and I really feel the benefit of an hour's session with this during the early winter evenings and dark days. Whilst they are relatively expensive, I believe the investment has been well made.

I am still seeing an NHS psychiatrist every 8-12 weeks and, whilst they were initially interested in my background, they too placed a great emphasis on treatment of depression by drugs. In addition, as with the GPs, they have rarely suggested any alternative therapies, aside from attending the local MIND centre to meet other people with depression.

Earlier, I talked about some research I conducted into adrenal and thyroid fatigue and the endocrine system as a whole and potential affect this could have on either causing or perpetuating depression. I had occasion to discuss this with the psychiatrist and his lack of knowledge on this matter was staggering to say the least. His comment "you probably know more about this than me" said it all and I felt horribly let down by the system. In fairness to the psychiatrist, he did call in the senior psychiatrist who at least understood what I was talking about but generally took no cognizance of the facts I was presenting, citing that this was in the realms of alternative medicine and, in any case, the NHS tests I had undertaken did not support my theories.

In summary, I believe that there is an over-reliance on medication to treat depression and an under-reliance on using alternative therapies. My experience of depression and its highs and lows confirm to me that the best results are achieved when drugs are used in conjunction with personal therapy, light remedies, exercise, diet and personal development. As far as personal therapy from a counsellor or therapist is concerned, I was fortunate enough in that I was able to pay for private treatment myself but what if that was not the case? Would I have been offered this on the NHS and, if so, how frequently would I have been able to see one? Not weekly I am sure.

In my opinion, overall the NHS has only offered me limited support in my battle with depression and it should be better, much better than this. Stress and depression affects a staggeringly high proportion of the population and is one of the major contributors to absence from work, not to mention the marriages and relationships that are destroyed, the number of people unnecessarily committing suicide and the time and resources already committed to dealing with the illness in the NHS. If there was a more complete and holistic approach to mental health care, particularly looking at preventative measures rather than reactive measures, it would be of immense value to both the lives of individuals and their families and to the economy as well.

I would like to point out that I am not unduly laying the blame for this situation at the doors of individuals but I am blaming the set-up, processes and systems of mental healthcare in this country.

Another important and significant factor in my levels of depression occurs at night. Most prevalent when I was working was restless leg syndrome, or Akathisia, which prevented me from getting off to sleep and was an extremely unpleasant and uncomfortable experience. This would involve me having to keep moving my legs in bed and nothing, but nothing, could relieve the symptoms other than complete exhaustion at, usually, around four or five in the morning. It was common when I was working due to the fact that I would be tense and stressed, constantly analysing my performance and behaviours, bearing in mind I was always attempting to hide my depression and to appear as 'normal' to outsiders. This restless leg syndrome and rumination about work led to extreme nightmares every night once sleep did come.

Usually, the nightmares involved either work or situations where I was in danger and unable to control the outcome of events. For example, a recurring nightmare would involve me confronting people, barbarian warriors, thugs, enemy soldiers and so forth, in which I would need to protect others, such as my family, innocent people, etc, but I would be unable to move my arms to defend either myself or the others. It was like they were stuck to my sides or they did not exist at all. All I could do was to move my shoulders or torso from side to side to no effect at all. There are recollections here of the time I was held down by those teenagers a long time ago while they stuffed grass down my throat. Here was I, the brave defender of the innocent and unprotected and I am powerless and impotent, unable to carry out my duties and drive off the assailants. This feeling would produce profuse sweating and unimaginable tension, racked with pain and guilt even though nobody was ever actually caught or hurt in the dream.

Another recurring dream is where I am being chased, again by barbarians or even giant snowballs and stones rolling down slopes getting bigger and bigger as they get closer and closer, but never getting caught. Always running, always looking back over my shoulder in sheer terror and fright, the gap between us always getting smaller and smaller but never reaching me, never a conclusion, always left in limbo, like standing on a precipice but never actually falling.

There were times I would be in the bridge of a large ship, travelling very fast and close to the shore, too close for comfort, and then having to navigate a narrow waterway that seemed too small for the ship. The speed would never drop, indeed it seemed to get faster and faster the closer it came to the shore and the waterway and I would be completely helpless to either steer the ship away from its imminent demise or reduce the speed and avoid running aground. As with the other dreams, there was never a running aground nor was there a conclusion, just perpetual danger, risk, suspense and fear.

These dreams, or rather nightmares, were significant in that, depending on the depth of realness and severity, they would adversely affect me when I awoke. These nightly experiences would determine how depressed I became that day. It would take a very long time during the day for the memories of the nightmares to dissipate and these flashbacks would consume an inordinate amount of my thoughts, perpetuating the feeling of fear and anxiety. No matter how hard I tried, these feelings of suspense, dread and terror would linger and linger, at times plunging me into utter despair. Then, of course, there was the knowledge each day that these nightmares would return again that night and future nights. All the while, the explanation as to what these bad dreams meant eluded me; I could think of no rational explanation or was I looking for the impossible? Are they meant to represent something significant from my past in this life, a future life or even from a previous life, if there is such a thing?

After talking to others with depression, it would appear that nightmares are a common occurrence and has a preponderance to affect the levels of their depression almost as equally as mine. I remember as a child of about seven having an ear infection with a raging temperature and experiencing a recurrent nightmare about a man and a robot on a motorcycle chasing after me and never actually catching me. Recognise a theme here? Terrified, I would take a stick to bed with me and sleep under the covers in a vain attempt to fend off the would-be attackers. This nightmare, and the ones I now have, are so real and vivid I believe that they actually exist even in a conscious state. During them I am constantly moving and shifting position in the bed, my wife often wakes me to try and snap me out of the ordeal. Usually, though, when I drift off again there I am right back where I was. I will often sweat profusely during the night. I'm even aware of the beads of perspiration running down my body onto the sheets, soaking them thoroughly. At times I have wondered whether I have wet the bed, the sheets and duvet cover being so damp.

I have managed to get some relief from these nightmares after talking to Alan, my therapist. He suggested that we could artificially manufacture a successful conclusion to the nightmares using a technique that involved going into a deep relaxed state. This process would begin by listening to some soft meditative music and controlled deep breathing and then slowly relaxing my mind and body to produce an altered state of consciousness. Alan would then talk to me, asking me to describe the nightmare and at the point of no conclusion he would enquire as to what would be required to end the never-ending dilemma. For example, if I was protecting a group of villagers from barbarian warriors and I was unable to use my arms to defend both them and me, I would imagine that my arms could in fact function perfectly normally and then I would be able to fight off the screaming horde of blood-thirsty savages. Alan would gently bring me back to a conscious state and check that I felt okay and was fully awake. There was an immediate sense of relief – not imagined but very real – that I had indeed staved off the slaughter of the innocents and good had prevailed over evil. There was also the relief that the nightmare had a conclusion, a good conclusion. To this day, I have never had this dream again. We repeated this process for the other recurring nightmares with equal success. What a joy and a revelation!

However, sadly that is not the end to my nightly suffering. I still have to endure nightmares every night but now they are different in content and context but retain a common theme – work. Since being on sick leave from work, it seems that there were unresolved issues, events, experiences and worries that are being replayed in my nightmares. Particularly stressful or pressured times and situations where I felt I could have or should have done better. Remember, I was a perfectionist then and I constantly analysed my own performance; did I do this right or could I have done that better? What should have I done differently? Maybe if I had taken a different tact or an alternative decision things would have turned out differently (better). This self-flagellation was both automatic and painful, then and now, and still haunts me to the point that when I remember these events I still feel sick in the pit of my stomach, my breathing accelerates and the palms of my hands go clammy and cold.

I beat myself up for not being more outspoken at work, for not saying what I really wanted to say but a combination of my depression, trying to avoid conflict, trying to be helpful and the political culture prevailing at work, kept me from being honest and forthright most of the time. There were many times I kept my peace in order to have a quiet life and afterwards I would severely castigate myself for this, particularly after work and into my nightmares. So much for a quiet life; the only ones who benefited were the others, not me, which was perverse to the extreme. Worse still, I realised this and did nothing. Sure, I would resolve each time to rectify this and promise myself I would speak up next time, always next time, only to do nothing next time. The more I promised and then did nothing, the harder I would be on myself, the more I would get frustrated, angry and resentful of myself on into the evening and again into my dreams. A vicious cycle continually gnawing away at my self-esteem.

Although most of the time I am an extremely patient and calm person on the outside, there is real anger lurking just beneath the surface, waiting to explode. The first time I realised the existence of this anger was when I was head boy at my secondary school and I saw the school's 'hardest' fifth former bullying some juniors with his gang of cronies. When I confronted him about his behaviour his reaction was to try and bully me, belittle me in front of his mates. At some point my patience and calmness deserted me in a rush of adrenaline and a fight ensued, although all I can recall is being pulled off the boy who was lying on the ground semi-conscious and badly beaten. I had no idea what happened during the previous few minutes – I had been in a blind rage and yet, now looking at what I had done I was mortified. Where did this anger come from, why did it just happen and worse still, what could have happened if I had not been stopped? This experience left me terrified and extremely aware of the latent temper and anger.

Perhaps my reluctance in future conflict situations to really display my true feelings has its roots in this sad event. I reasoned that if it has happened before, it could happen again and I might not be able to control it. However, the end result was that any expression of anger and/or temper was directed inside rather than outside and it was me, ultimately, that paid the price. The more I kept my feelings to myself and avoided potential conflict situations, the less I became involved in heated exchanges or arguments, the less skilled I became at dealing with them and thus, I avoided them even more. This was particularly true at work where I always tried to mediate, compromise or just give in and, returning to my nightmares, this inadequacy would haunt me nightly and still does. My nightmares still have me being meek and mild, confronted by a bully of a boss – loud, brash, and unreasonable – and I would be helpless to defend myself, arms pinned to my sided as before; I wanted to say what I really thought but no words were forthcoming.

I would toss and turn all night, playing these old tapes over and over again, completely impotent, useless and frustrated. Waking up brought no relief as the memory of the dream would hang around me for hours, like dark foreboding clouds that overshadow and consume you. To this day, I still have these dreams and no amount of going to bed thinking of good things or promising myself that I will have nice dreams will make them go away. They feel like a prison sentence with no hope of release for good behaviour; every night feels like being trapped in your cell with no way out, no relief, not even probation.

This inwardly directed anger was like a cancer, eating away at me, destroying my soul, my spirituality, my essence of being. It became such that if something went wrong, it must be my fault, such was the complete lack of confidence I had in myself and my abilities. Others would often pay me compliments for my efficiency, organisation, calmness and other virtues I am almost too embarrassed to mention, but I would think they were just saying that to be nice, but inside I would be saying they should see the real me. Just like a swan swimming in the lake, gliding gracefully on the top but paddling furiously underneath. Who was right? At the time I thought I was but now I think they were. But hindsight is a wonderful thing – it goes on my Christmas list each year without success.

The saddest aspect of my handling anger was that I was more likely to be angry with my loved ones than I was with others, such as people at work or complete strangers. This is one of the most regrettable side effects of my depression and, perversely, makes me angry with myself, perpetuating the cycle of inward anger and frustration. How could I treat those special people like this? I can only feebly excuse myself by reasoning that I was always looking for acceptance from others (fear of rejection) and took it for granted that I already had my loved ones' acceptance, and therefore it was okay to be angry with them. With work colleagues I had a reputation for being mild mannered and controlled and I could not possibly let them see me otherwise, could I? I had a reputation to maintain and, perhaps, a promotion to chase. After all, promotion meant better pay, better benefits, better company car, better status and all these material things would improve the lives of my family. What a contradiction that is, so obvious now but I could not see this then. What a fool I was!

Chapter 8

Perspectives

During periods of depression I would feel insecure about myself, consistently juggling my ability to do things – at work, home and socially – and I would feel self-conscious about the way I looked. I do not know why these feelings manifested themselves but they are inextricably linked to depression and yet nor do I care, other than to remind myself that I need to be aware of these thoughts and how they impact on my view of myself. I must remember that insecurities are a normal part of life for everyone, even those who appear to be extremely self-assured, and I have found that when I do this I can step back from the uncertainty that lies within and take a more realistic look at myself. I have always striven and desired to improve and better myself to avoid rejection and to be accepted but again this is actually a natural response that arises when we begin to compare our lives to those of other people. I always assumed that, due to my depression, it seemed, for example, that I did not have as much going for me as my colleagues, friends or family. In truth, what we think we see about another person is actually what they want us to notice. They may be putting on a mask or a disguise as I have done for years, they may be trying to make things in their lives seem better than they are. If I was to look at their lives more closely rather than exclusively thinking about myself, I would probably realise that they are human, full of glorious imperfections that make them who they are. This has taken me some time to recognise but now each time I feel my own uncertainties arise or surface, I take a deep breath and acknowledge each of my own gifts, even depression, and this has helped me become more holistically centred. I can now see the wonders that lie within and slowly, ever so slowly, my inner beauty is starting to shine through into the world – just a glimmer, but it is glowing.

When I held a detailed mirror to my life and compared myself to others, I was not able to see the things that made me truly unique. Giving myself permission to appreciate all the universe has given me, however, has made me feel more secure about myself and begin to use my gifts to their fullest potential. The time I have been off work has allowed me to reflect on my new life, how I have lived my past life and what it has all meant. It has also given me the space I needed to consider my true purpose in life, the 'why' of my existence and the 'why' of my experiences, both in and out of depression.

During my time off work I have read many books on the subject of depression, self-help books about healing oneself and technical books on counselling and coaching. I have also ploughed through books on spirituality and meditation. All of these books have taught me many valuable lessons, some more than others, but all this knowledge distils down to the fact that depression is a solitary illness where you are alone and only you can truly know the shame, guilt, fear, anger, jealousy and hate. They may preach practical solutions and remedies about how one may battle the condition, how one may decrease the symptoms, how one may overcome depression in the end and lead a 'normal' life. When I read these well-meaning literatures I am often filled with optimism and enthusiasm – have I at last found the real solution to my problem? I practise and practise the teachings contained within and convince myself that this is the way forward but my heartfelt hopes are always dashed when there is either only temporary relief or no relief at all.

However, what the books have given me is a wider knowledge of the illness and the importance of putting everything into perspective, which is one of the first things I lose when I am depressed. 'Perspective' – an interesting word that means to understand how important things are in relation to others, a particular way of seeing something, a mental view. It comes from the Latin word 'perspectiva ars', the science of optics, which is the science concerned with vision and the behaviour of light. For me, depression has robbed me of the ability to put things into perspective. I always look on the dark side, always expect the worst, always expect failure. Lack of perspective and 360 degree vision has made me an expert in guilt. I have consistently failed myself and others, I have failed to live up to my expectations and those of others, such as my family. Lack of perspective has made me punish myself for all my stupidities and so-called failures, whether real or imagined.

The Greek philosopher, Epictetus, said "it is not the things in themselves which trouble us, but the opinions we have about these things". How right he is. This loss of perspective has led me to have negative opinions, regardless of the situation; it could always have been better. The question then becomes, if I can change my opinions or perspectives, can I break out from behind the barrier of depression?

Probably so, I cry out, but how can I do this and the many other well-meaning treatments for depression, when I am in a state of depression, stuck in that dark pit with wet, slimy walls that will just not let me climb them to reach that Shangri-la called 'normal'? Every thought I have is tainted by my depression. I have taught myself and practised for many years to think as a depressive and to think 'normal' is alien to me. How then can I change my opinions and perspective when I am in this place? I absolutely agree that it is the right thing to do but how do I do it?

In Dorothy Rowe's excellent book *Depression, The Way Out of Your Prison*, she describes six real, absolute and immutable truths that depressed people hold dear, which are:

1. No matter how good and acceptable I appear to be, I am really bad, evil, valueless, unacceptable to myself and other people.
2. Other people are such that I must fear, hate and envy them
3. Life is terrible and death is worse.

4. Only bad things happened to me in the past and only bad things will happen to me in the future.
5. It is wrong to get angry.
6. I must never forgive anyone, least of all myself.

I totally agree with these with the exception of No 3 – I have believed that life is terrible and death would be a release, but more of this later. When you hold these opinions so strongly and so consistently, it is damned hard to change them. But changing them is a must if I want to get better. I have built these opinions into values by which I have lived my life and only I can alter them. But in depression you shun the sympathy and concern of others and you deny yourself the love of oneself. Others may be there to hold out a comforting hand and offer you help and support but you will not let them past the barrier in order to help. Therefore, it is down to me but after all the reflection and soul-searching I have done recently I am becoming aware that I do know that the power does lie within me to start climbing the walls of the pit and emerge victorious. The climb will be long, hard, challenging, with many setbacks along the way, but triumph I will.

Chapter 9

Stepping Back from the Edge

Before I start on my journey of redemption, it is worth going back once again to describe some of my blackest moments when I truly believed that life was terrible but death would be a release. Thoughts of death and suicide are common amongst people suffering from depression and, indeed, many people sadly succumb to these thoughts. I was no different. There have been times when my depression was so bad I could see no way out other than to end it all, my suffering and the suffering I was inflicting on others, particularly my wife. These deepest, darkest times would come for no particular reason and they would hit me like an express train at rush hour. My thoughts would be in complete turmoil, decisions impossible to make, my body wracked by cold sweats, knotted stomach and weak knees. All I knew was that I had to escape, get away from it all, whatever 'it' was. I couldn't cope anymore, I could not even decide if I wanted a cup of tea or coffee. I would become uncontrollably emotional, crying like a baby, unable to even wipe my runny nose. All I could think about was how futile my existence was, there was no longer any reason to live, no purpose to fulfil, I was useless and the world would be a better place without me. I pitied myself and I hated this; men should not pity themselves, they should pity others, therefore I was not a man and if I was not a man I did not deserve to live.

Thoughts of death would come a great deal of the time and both terrified me and allured me. It looked attractive as it would put an end to the misery. But what of my family; could I bear to cause them more suffering than I already had? But in those states I was completely ambivalent to the feelings of those I would leave behind. I have stood at the edge of cliffs in readiness to jump onto the rocks or sea below, almost feeling the sense of relief and joy of sailing peacefully through the air to oblivion. I would imagine myself flying, like a seagull on the thermals, graceful and silent in the currents of air, getting ever closer to my final destination and absolution.

I would stand on the precipice for what seemed hours, but was probably only a few minutes, swept with a variety of emotions that would swirl around like a whirlwind in my mind. They say that a person's life flashes before them seconds before death and this was how it seemed to me. Memories of my childhood, teenage and later years flooded into my consciousness, like a film on super fast-forward. Tears were in my eyes, my heart was heavy and my lungs heaving. All I needed to do was just take one step, one small step and I would be gone forever. Why, on each occasion that I stood perched in readiness to end it all, I decided to stop at this point I do not really know. It certainly would have been easier to jump and die than to continue with the struggle against depression. But stop I did and I would take a backward step and accept the challenge to take my depression head on and continue to find a way to become a man again, to be a husband, a father and son again, whatever that would bring.

Writing about these desperate times now has been incredibly difficult and stirred up some very painful memories but as I think about these recollections in greater depth, I firmly believe that this has been a cathartic release for me. Perhaps now I can let those memories and experiences go and start the process of forgiving myself. I certainly do not regret the decisions not to jump and, instead, see them as chances to alter the destiny of my life and the lives of those around me. Ultimately, when I look back and question why I did not jump, I believe it was for my family and not for me. I had made this choice for their sake and now I just had to get better. I remember thinking about my daughter and who would give her away when she got married, thinking about my sons and their children, and my wife living by herself, maybe even meeting someone else. In the end, I believe I am a stronger person for taking the difficult path and this was a defining moment in my journey through life.

To me suicide was not about giving up and dying; it was about making the choice to give life another try, even if it meant further punishment for me and others. My suicide would have sent a message to my family that they would have been better off without me, that I did not love them enough to keep going and find my way out of my living hell. All my life I had tried to better myself, to improve, to be accepted rather than rejected but suicide contradicted this and stood for failure when things got tough. Since these times, I have learnt that life is worth living, you can make a contribution regardless of how you feel. Death will come anyway and there is no point in ending it prematurely.

Whilst I no longer think of suicide as much as I did, I still think about death and at times I am rather ambivalent about my own health, particularly when it comes to continuing with my smoking. I no longer fear death as I used to and accept my own mortality. Whether this is because I have become more spiritual recently I do not know, but I now believe in the fact that I have had previous lives and that in this life my experiences with depression were pre-ordained and that I have gone through what I have gone through in order that I must help others with the illness. This is my purpose in life and now that I have realised this I no longer fear death as it is my future and I do not fear the future. This newly discovered purpose of mine to help and enlighten others and banish the ill-judged stigma attached to depression is what spurs me on.

To realise my purpose has opened many doors for me, particularly the doorway to a new life and this is inspiring me with hope rather than fear. This realisation has been both a rude awakening and a beam of light. All my life, until now, I had never considered that I needed a purpose or indeed had one. It was always enough to know that I would get married, have a family, get a job, provide for my family, work hard to get promotion in order to possess material wealth, and so on and so on. Some people call it the 'rat race' or 'life's merry-go-round' – I call it the treadmill of soullessness. I lost my soul and my innate sense of being whilst I became a slave to prosperity, success and external recognition. It took a breakdown to recognise that this was truly not why I was here. I could have had different kinds of prosperity, success and external recognition without being stuck on the treadmill of soullessness. Would I still have had depression? Who knows, but what is important is not that I look back and wonder 'what if?' but to look firstly to the present and enjoy the riches of what I have; and secondly, to look to the future with hope for myself and others like me.

I no longer see depression as a curse, I no longer see myself as a victim of others or circumstances, nor do I see regret or sorrow. I see depression as a gift, bestowed upon myself by a higher force or power and, most of all, I see myself as being special. I do not believe depression to be a problem but rather as a challenge, one that must be accepted and faced head on. Depression is an opportunity to discover oneself, to see life from another perspective, one that is not afforded to all and sundry, albeit that perspective can seem painful, unjust and a solitary experience. It is an opportunity to learn and develop sensitivities about oneself and about others, to create a self that is multi-faceted and worldly. Walking with depression as a constant companion no longer holds any fears for me, I am beginning to embrace it and treat it with respect for it is within me but it is not me.

Now that I know these things, I can start to tame the black dog, shrink it down in size and begin to master it. Though it may always be with me, as long as I recognise this I can be in control. I can be in charge and I can decide what effect it has on me. I have the choices, the options and the decisions are mine and mine alone. While this may seem easy to articulate and theorise, I appreciate that, in practice, it is harder to put into reality and those of you who are reading this book who have depression will know that. There are times when my depression grips me hard and in these times it is easy to forget that you have choices, options and hard decisions to make, but make them you can. When it strikes, for whatever reason, in whatever circumstances, I go back to basics and accept the fact that I am not feeling too good and stop resisting the depression. Resistance for me proves futile and merely stokes the fires of depression and pours oil on the internal flames that burn fiercely inside. Acceptance allows me to quench the inferno, regain my perspective and balance my life and gradually put the black feelings back into the corner where they belong, on a lead and tethered.

For too long I was ashamed of the fact that I had depression and would frequently tell lies or be economical with the truth when asked if I was feeling alright. This was particularly true once I went on sick leave from my employer and people would enquire as to how work was going or why I was at home when previously I had spent a great deal of time away. Now, however, I am no longer ashamed, feel guilty or fearful of telling the truth. After all, if I had a broken leg and had a plaster cast I would not be too embarrassed to tell them what was wrong, so why should I not tell them that I have depression. True – many people, when told I have depression do have difficulties in knowing what to say in response and some feel downright uncomfortable. Some react as if you have told them someone close has died and become tongue-tied and awkward but this tells me more about them than it does about me. I have become adept at spotting the awkwardness and use this opportunity to tell them more about depression and how it affects me. I now use these instances to live my purpose and enlighten the unenlightened or ignorant. This approach has worked well for me and rather than rejecting me, my earlier fear, people are now more understanding and usually more inquisitive.

The more I have become open and honest the more I am finding that I am meeting people who have, have had or know someone else who suffer from depression. In truth, the perception of my fears from being open and honest has been far worse than the reality. This has greatly surprised me but I guess I do not fully understand why. Perhaps generally people are more understanding and considerate than I previously gave them credit for. Perhaps my earlier experiences in employment when I heard managers, senior and junior, casting doubts on periods of absence due to depression by other employees has clouded my judgment and that this was the exception rather than the rule. Whatever the reason, I am now resolved that I will no longer hide my depression from anyone, nor will I feel guilty, ashamed or embarrassed. If others have an issue with it then it is for them to deal with how they feel or what they believe; those are their options, choices and decisions to make – not mine, I can only be responsible for myself.

The old cliché "sticks and stones will break my bones but names will never hurt me" may be true for some but it is an untruth for people with depression. I have always been concerned about what others thought and said about me for reasons of acceptance and rejection I have previously outlined. The very thought that others did not hold me in high regard or that I did not live up to their expectations would fill me with dread and has even made my depression worse at times. If I made a mistake, completed a job to less than perfection or disappointed them in any way, this would play on my mind for days and even weeks. I would search for explanations, reasons and justifications of what I had or had not done, punishing myself by working harder or doing more than was expected in order to redeem myself. Words or opinion were like a sword being plunged into my inner self, expunging any confidence and self-esteem I may have had and reinforcing the messages of self-doubt and criticism. If they say so then surely this must be true, they know better than I.

Not now. I have come to realise that everyone makes mistakes, performs to less than perfection and do disappoint others from time to time. This is what life is all about. How can I learn if I do not make any mistakes? How will I improve and grow if I do not meet others' expectations all the time. Nobody is perfect, there is no such thing as perfection so why do I aspire to be perfect? Surely it is enough to do one's best and it is okay to do so without berating oneself. Now I accept my mistakes as part of the challenges of life, now I do not seek perfection but rather just do my best and now I do not fear what others say about me. Words, now, are but a blunt sword that cannot pierce my inner-self and rekindle thoughts of depression. Perspective, I tell myself, it is all a question of perspective and, contrary to my earlier beliefs, they are not cast in stone, they are mine and mine alone and if I need to adjust them, then it is right to do so, for me rather than for anyone else.

Chapter 10

Inside or Outside? – The Dichotomy

Deep down, I always have believed that I am not good enough and that to be accepted by others I had to work hard to be good. I would look at others with a mixture of envy and hate – envy because they seemed to be so comfortable within themselves and with others and I hated them in equal measure because they had what I thought I did not have. I always imagined that only good things happened to them whereas only bad things happened to me. As a result, I would grossly distort any setbacks, mistakes or performance less than perfection, twisting, turning and bloating these out of all proportion. Oh, how I wanted to be 'normal' like everyone else, to live a life with fun, humour and joy. I was so locked up in my prison of depression that these things eluded me completely and, in any case, I thought that people were used to seeing me the way I was – quiet, distant, even aloof – that to be anything else would raise suspicion and draw attention to myself. Heaven forbid that they may talk about me as I would, therefore, lose the much-sought-after anonymity.

This dichotomy became a real paradox for me. On the one hand I craved to be the same as others and yet on the other hand I wanted – no needed – the life of obscurity that had, apparently, served me so well over the years. After years of depression, I had created, learnt and practised the persona of a depressed person and it had become my way of living, it had become my comfort zone and I was scared to leave it, even if that meant denying myself laughter, happiness and carefree living.

Standing behind my barrier I would carefully observe the rest of the world, watching people closely as they casually interacted with each other. I became very sensitive to body language and, as previously explained, words, and how they were said and in what context. It was as if I was in a theatre or a cinema watching scenes played out by actors for an audience of one. I became adept at knowing who to speak to or approach just by the way they looked, carried themselves or even dressed. Intuition guided me to recognise people with positive energy and those with negative energy and allowed me to carefully select those I should avoid. This 'gift' served me well up to a point and I was rarely wrong in judging people but it became yet another obstacle to having normal relations. The extent to which I used these sensitivities and intuition caused problems between Jennie and me, on occasions when meeting new people or friends of hers whom I judged negatively. I would make no effort to socialise with them, just talking to them was an effort, and I would come across as rude and unwelcoming. But this was also true of my own family too; a sister of mine recently admitted that she did not know if I even liked her. How sad it is that my own kith and kin should think that of me and how ashamed I was that I had given this impression, which was entirely not intentional.

The end result of safely watching others from behind my barrier and not socially interacting with others unless on my terms, meant in reality that I continued to have very few people I could call friends, a habit I started back in my late teens, where this story really started. That is not to say I did not care for others or others did not care for me but I would always keep them at arm's length, rarely, for example, letting them into my home, which I saw as my haven. Visitors would only come to the house to see either Jennie or the children, never me. At the time I neither saw this as an issue or unusual, after all this was the way I wanted it to be. But in hindsight, I now see how much poorer my past life has been without the company and friendship of others who could have brightened my days and lifted my moods, even sharing somehow in my illness. But hindsight is a wonderful thing, seemingly blessed to only those in higher authority.

The weeks, months and years I have been at home on sick leave have given me the opportunity to seriously reflect and contemplate a number of values I held true as a depressed person, such as limiting social contact. With my wife at work, my daughter at school and my two sons at university, I would spend long periods at home on my own. Although I filled my time with household duties, cooking, shopping, reading and DIY, I actually started to crave human contact. Early in my sick leave we bought a super West Highland Terrier puppy, called Lucy, who gave me great pleasure and distraction from my loneliness, but it still was not the same. When she was old enough to take out for walks many people would take an interest in her and talk to me, which at first was rather daunting, but after a short while was really welcome and started to give me confidence in catching people's eyes and initiating greetings with them. It surprised me how good a simple 'good morning' and a warm smile could make me feel, even from a complete stranger. What was all the fuss about, I asked myself, this was easier than I thought and was doing me good; again the perception was worse than the reality.

Now, 20 months on from getting Lucy, she is my constant companion around the house and on long walks. She has the ability to brighten up my day and make me smile, both externally and internally. She will never know how much difference she has made to a depressed person, giving me inspiration, unbounded friendship and unconditional love. She really has been a beacon of light in a very long dark tunnel of despair and she is part of the process of guiding me through to the light and hopefully the end of the journey.

I mentioned above walking Lucy and this is part of a return to physical activities that I let lapse in the last few years of working. Squash is another activity that I am returning to and finding helpful in my recovery. During the particularly deep periods of depression I would attempt to play but I found it a struggle to socially engage with my partners, initiate matches and generally enjoy the occasion. More often than not, my performance would be affected by my mood and my mood was affected by my performance. Because of my perfectionism I had to play to a certain standard and if this was not achieved I would get angry with myself, become aggressive and sullen, banging my racket on the wall or floor and swearing. Not much fun for my opponents but, what the hell, they were okay, they did not have depression, I reasoned. Why people bothered to play with me I do not know but a couple of guys I can call my friends did persevere with me and real credit to them. Bill and Jason stuck with me and were very patient and understanding, even when I must have bored them to death with my tales of woe and despair. But they, like Lucy, have been instrumental in the seeds of recovery I now feel are starting to shoot and I will be eternally grateful for their unconditional friendship.

I have also returned to team squash recently despite my anxieties around groups of people, particularly when I am aware that they know I had depression and was off work. Without exception, my team mates accepted me as I was, without judgement, ridicule or scepticism and are always prepared to genuinely ask how I am and they have no fear or stigma on openly discussing depression. How different they are to those that I worked with constantly for so many years who were either ashamed, afraid or embarrassed to do the same. I now look forward to team games as I know I will be safe and comfortable in the company of people who feel at ease with me, I feel at ease with them and who make me feel 'normal'. I now consider my team mates as friends and this is another positive step towards recovery.

To the uninitiated, these admissions may seem either mundane or laughable in the extreme, but to me these are huge steps on the journey I am now taking where existing outdated or non-helpful values are being challenged and changed. This process of change is one of evolution rather than revolution, out of sheer necessity and for the maintenance of a sense of order. Too many changes, too soon and together create a sense of confusion in my identity and sense of well-being and each untrue value has to be tackled slowly and carefully and after considerable evaluation. In a sense, some of my traits that assisted my descent into depression, attention to detail, perfectionism, a strong desire to be always organised and religiously task-oriented, are now actually playing an active role in my recovery. Values and beliefs I believe are no longer useful are carefully logged in my journal and I set about appraising them as I would a project at work, but with a significant difference. I no longer look to achieve these tasks and activities for someone else's benefit, acceptance, approval or recognition. These tasks and activities are for me and me alone and I will know whether they are appropriate and relevant to my personal development and I do not fear rejection, whatever the outcome.

Walking, particularly with my wife and Lucy, has become an important activity in my daily life and has the effect of raising my serotonin levels. I especially like walking by the sea, as I always have done, but now I can really appreciate the calming influence it has on me. Just watching the sea, in any state, calm or rough, has an almost hypnotic effect on my state of mind. Nature has provided the sea with a power and tranquillity that I seek; it is uncomplicated and serene yet it is attractive and alluring. I have even been able to go back to those very cliffs and spots that I contemplated suicide and laid those ghosts to rest, banished to the outer limits of my consciousness.

There are still days and occasionally the odd week when depression returns but each time it comes back it loses some of its intensity. I have been collecting a box of tools that I can use to help me cope with these periods; it is a case of just selecting the right tool at the right time to fix the issue or challenge that has caused my relapse. It is by no means a complete tool box but at least it is there and I can dip into it at any time; and I can keep adding to it as time goes by; and I get better at spotting appropriate tools for future use. To use an analogy, the engine may not be firing on all cylinders, but it is running and now needs tuning, adjustment and ongoing maintenance to keep it in good running order.

My breakdown over two years ago was a sign that what I was doing was not right and that if I kept doing what I had always been doing I would always get the same result. The breakdown was a pivotal moment in my life and I see it as a second opportunity to do the right things and for it to be a dawning of a new and better life. With the help of my family, particularly my wife, and my new friends I have accepted this opportunity with open arms and acknowledged that change was inevitable if I was to have a chance of recovery. I am still on anti-depressants and, after trying many types, I believe my current one has finally taken the edge off my depression. But this is not enough on its own, I have to take some, if not all, responsibility for making personal changes at a deeper, conscious and unconscious, level and that my behaviour, emotions, thoughts and feelings will need to be altered permanently in order for me to rid myself of depression and climb out of that black pit. Those dark clouds will never part and allow the sun to shine through if I do nothing, I cannot and will not just accept that I will never get better. I owe this not just to myself, but to all those around me who believe in me, supported me, stayed with me and above all love me.

Earlier in my account, I detailed the relationship, or lack of, that I had with my boss, George. At the time I viewed George as my tormentor, someone who in many ways I thought had added to my depression. Now, when I look back, I can see another dimension that was not apparent whilst I was working with him. It felt that his attitude and behaviour towards me, and others, was detrimental to my well-being, self-esteem and confidence. I was wrong. I now accept that I must take responsibility for feeling like this. This is because I had choices; I could choose to allow him to make me feel like this or I could choose not to. I chose the former, I gave him permission to steal my personal power and to grant him the right to affect the way I thought and felt. That is not his fault – he was what he was, he was doing what he thought was right with the options his experiences of the world have given him. The fact that the courses of actions and his conduct that he selected did not agree with me and the courses of action I took say more about me than it did about him.

Today, I see George as a teacher rather than a tormentor or scourge. I have learnt that I reacted the way I did because I failed to make the correct choices in responding to the way he was. He cannot be held responsible for my emotions and ways of thinking, only I can take that responsibility. He has taught me that, in future, I must hold myself accountable for my decision making and that I have alternatives available to me if only I stop and remember this. I also believe that I had the potential to influence his behaviour if I was more honest and true to myself and to him. I could have discussed how I was allowing him to affect me and tell him how I would have liked to have been treated. I never gave him this opportunity and it is I who is poorer for this. This was a hard but valuable lesson for me to learn, but the harder the lesson the greater the learning.

Chapter 11

Meaning to Existence

Discovering my true purpose in life, to write this book, to enlighten others about depression and help others as others have helped me, gives me meaning to my existence, and the will and the enthusiasm to carry on making progress. Writing this book has been a wonderfully cathartic exercise, which whilst recalling many demons from my former life, has allowed me to exorcise them and put them into perspective and out of mind. I now have an identity, a true identity rather than a fake one I have carried around with me for so many years, the one that says 'I must be perfect and work hard and I must do things for my family and others before myself so they will go on needing me and not reject me'. My new identity allows me to believe that I must be kind and compassionate with myself, that I need not be perfect and all things to all people and, in addition, nor am I unacceptable or as bad as I once thought I was.

I am beginning to learn that it is okay to relax, do something that pleases me and to enjoy life. This learning has come about by the realisation that I have choices, more choices than I thought of before, and these can be for me and it is okay. If I can be kind to myself I am then able to let others be kind to me as well, without feeling obliged to repay them in some way or be humiliated because they might think me weak. After years of denying any self-love, the art of relaxing and enjoying the moment has not come easily and I often catch myself thinking about what needs to be done or what I should or could be doing instead. Even reading the paper can make me feel anxious that this is time not well spent or productive so it is challenging to force yourself to go from front cover to back cover and I have to remind myself that it is actually okay to do this. No-one is watching, no-one is evaluating or analysing what I am doing; for God's sake I am 50 years old yet I feel like a naughty school boy at times. Grow up, make your choices, do the right things for you and act like an adult.

To do this requires trust – trust in yourself and being responsible for your actions. Yes, years ago I trusted my friends but they still managed to throw me out of the tent and let me fend for myself, but that was then and this is now. I have read that it is not what happens to you that affects you but it is how you interpret what happens to you that affects you. For me, this means that the event all those years ago needs to be put into context and perspective and that I should and can change my interpretation of what happened on that holiday. I can take a less serious view of the incident; nobody died after all. Don't all teenagers fall out from time to time, even adults for that matter. Surely, I have blown it out of all proportion and no longer is it useful to see it as anything else but a tiff between friends.

Returning to trusting in myself, once I have belief in this trust then I can start trusting others. The very fact that I am now open about the fact that I have depression is demonstrating to me that the newfound trust I have in myself is evidence that I am actually trusting others. I have read somewhere that depression thrives on secrecy and I can see the truth in this. Being open and honest with others is an enlightening process in which, once again, the general reaction I have received is far better than the perception or fear. Time and again this is happening; many of my old beliefs and fears are just not coming true. It is okay to trust others after all, it is okay to trust yourself and it is okay if now and again someone will abuse that trust. That is just life and I will have to accept it; resistance is futile and will only take me back down the snake to the starting position again, depression, looking for those elusive ladders.

Far better to avoid the snakes and climb the ladders, let the real me come out of the closet and reclaim my rightful place in society.

I fully realise that, as the Chinese philosopher, Lao-tzu, once said: "The journey of a thousand miles begins with the first step", my journey will be a long one and that it is likely that I may, from time to time, slide back down the snake. The secret will be how quickly I can climb back up the ladder and that when this happens I do not see it as a setback, I see it as a new challenge, new opportunity to learn new things about myself and, above all, to not make it mean anything.

One benefit of being able to talk to others about my depression is that others then feel able to share their secret and tell me about *their* depression.

It seems that now that I am open about my illness, this has opened the closet doors and many others are coming forward and describing their experiences of depression. Being able to confide in others is, by mutual agreement, a very liberating experience and, whilst we all have different backgrounds and knowledge of depression, we have similar tales to tell, and this adds significance to our lives by knowing others also suffer. What is incredibly sad is that, in my knowledge, many people are either unable or unwilling to tell their story because they cannot find the courage to speak out and/or cannot find someone to talk to that they trust. The people I have encountered who are both willing and able to share their experiences are greatly relieved to be able to talk about how they feel, what they have and are going through and, in some cases, are desperate for help and understanding.

In a sense, by writing this book, I and the other contributors are talking to you, the wider world, and you are bearing witness to the journeys we have, and may still be undertaking, and to our reality, pluck, distress and torment. Hopefully, by reading this book, you will allow yourself to be open-minded and be able to relate in some way to another's suffering and to be also understanding to the fact that depressives live their lives differently to you.

The mere fact that I have written this account proves to me, and I hope to you as well, that it has taken a great deal of courage to share my experiences with you and that this display of intrepidity is evidence I am on the path and am taking those first few steps. I have laid bare my innermost thoughts and feelings and even some secrets that at the beginning of this book I thought I would never reveal but I sincerely hope that by doing so it gives inspiration to others who have depression and a better understanding of its debilitating effects to those of you who do not.

Following my story are the personal journeys of others, both those that also suffer or have suffered and those that have lived with those who endure depression, and they too have displayed great heroism and awakening in coming forward and sharing their worldliness with you. I would like to publicly thank these contributors and to praise the courage they too have shown.

Although this is the end of my story, it is actually only the beginning to a rich and meaningful rest of my life, one that I am looking forward to with hope and without fear. Depression has provided me with opportunity and inspiration and for this I am grateful and I never believed in those darkest days that this would be the case. Out of adversity comes triumph.

Jennie's Story:
The Perspective from Outside the Barrier

I always knew there was something different about Steve!

He was always very private and seemed to be holding back, almost to the point of being aloof. This made him interesting and attractive to me, although I felt others were wary of him, which only served to make him even more irresistible because I could present to the rest of the world that only I was privy to him. But actually, I was not. Nobody was. His aloofness was interesting and yet at the same time both intriguing and surprising; I was always left wondering what, if anything, he was hiding. In the early days of our relationship it never occurred to me that a problem with mental health may have been behind this detachment.

The fact that he had depression never entered my head. How could it? I was blissfully ignorant of severe mental health problems. The first time I realised that this problem existed I typically thought that this must be my fault. I started reading articles about depression and its symptoms and they fitted him to a tee. I broached the subject with him and he admitted that he also felt he was suffering with depression. I was confused and felt terribly guilty that I was to blame because I could not make him happy, that I must have done something to cause it.

I came to realise that my emotions towards him did not change when I discovered he had depression but rather it was the feelings towards me that had changed. I felt inadequate, particularly when I watched other couples interact so well and happily. I have been amazed how they can behave towards each other and they do not seem to get depression, although to be honest I do not really know, I am only guessing.

Looking back, I could even pinpoint times or incidents that would justify my guilt or blame, even uselessness. These could be as simple as a difference of opinion, which would cause an argument and that would lead him into depression. Maybe I spent too much money and this would worry him and add to his stress levels. I even felt that having my friends and family visiting our home would upset him and make him depressed. When I went out I would worry that I had been away too long and he might get cross with me and then he would not speak to me for days and weeks. I even remember a specific incident when I was supposed to hold up a picture rail while he secured it to the wall and it fell down and hit him on the head. This seemed to send him deep into depression but from my perspective I could see this as annoying but no reason for depression.

Because I believed the blame lay with me, I thought I needed to redeem myself, perhaps try harder to make life more pleasant and problem-free for him. I started consciously thinking about what and how I said things to Steve. I strived to point out the positive things in our lives, such as our lovely children, our beautiful home, etc, and to encourage him to have what he wanted, to do the things he wanted to do, and so on. I would endeavour to buy nice foods as treats, but this was not easy for me with three children to bring up as well as the ups and downs that come with ongoing financial strains of a home to run. Still I felt that it was completely my responsibility rather than his as I must have caused this illness somehow.

On holiday one year at our caravan in North Cornwall, Steve was lower than usual, which I could not understand. This was our holiday, after all; yet he was very depressed.

We went walking one day and stopped to buy some hot chocolate and, in desperation, I ordered his with extra marshmallows thinking this would cheer him up. But of course it did not. I can think of so many pathetic attempts on my part to put things right that so obviously now would never work. In a vain attempt at alleviating my guilt I sometimes imagined that they did work and this would temporarily make me feel better, prompting me to keep trying.

Lucky for me, I have not had depression but this has meant that I cannot fully understand that no amount of extra marshmallows can make things right. I know differently now, I've learnt so much about his depression; in fact, together we have learnt so much. This education process is ongoing all the time. I'm still absorbing what depression is and how it affects Steve, still trying to justify his behaviour and desperately attempting to understand it. It has also been very frightening for me at times because I would imagine the worst possible outcome, such as him harming himself in some way. I have had to learn to distinguish between irrational and rational behaviour, never seeming to get it just right, it is always just a judgement. At times I feel so sad for Steve yet at times I am so very angry with him, but mostly now I no longer feel the need to feel like this. But there are times, even very recently, when I feel as if I could have nipped the current bout of depression in the bud had I acted differently. But I am only human.

Painfully I have watched him smoke, drink too much, eat too much, eat too little, experiment with his medication and so on. I have had to justify his behaviour to our children but they had their own opinions and they too have had to watch their father seemingly destroy himself. I discovered it was quite a fine line between protecting them and keeping them informed of depression and what it was doing to him. Steve's behaviour alienated us and I felt I was at a distance watching him wreck himself and there was not a thing I could do about it.

I almost accepted this but I cannot just stand by and do nothing. The smoking, in particular, I still see as an utter selfish act on his part. Because he feels bad or is low he smokes but both our children and I, who abhor smoking, have to just stand by and watch. What about our feelings? We have nursed him through depression and in the future we will have to nurse him through cancer. This is not fair on us! Selfish! How dare he?! Depression has made him irrational and desperate; I see now he was trying anything and everything to ease his pain, a pain we know nothing about, we cannot see, feel or touch. I did think that these relieving strategies were effective for a short while and that it was worth it. That is apart from smoking because that upsets everyone.

This – Steve's – mental health problem we have in our family has been a real test of relationships. It goes without saying what pressure there has been on our marriage. The – his – lack of communication, the rejection, the lack of fun and laughter et al, has greatly affected our social life. I have long stopped inviting family and friends to visit although I have become devious and planned visits when I knew he would not be around. Many times I have declined invitations to socialise and I am aware that invitations from others have become less and less over the years, which I find upsetting.

This depression has affected our financial state as well. He was a high-flyer with a well paid job and a posh car. Now Steve has left paid employment due to ill health and has become self-employed everything has changed and it will be a huge adjustment for us as a family. Our daughter recently asked me if we were going to be poor. However, I still see Steve as an achiever and I am also quite excited about the future, almost optimistic, and have faith in him to be successful even with depression. We will still have to work hard to manage this but he has accomplished so much already with depression. He has succeeded because he is very dedicated and such a hard worker, although we now know that this was also part of the depression problem for him.

The responsibility of keeping our family okay through this hugely difficult time falls solely with me. Others can, and do, support in different ways, but no-one can share this responsibility with me. I have been fortunate to have good friends and family and they have supported me greatly through these times. I have done, and at times still do, feel very lonely and scared. Where will this all end? Up until now my inner strength has got me through and will have to keep me going even longer. I am also very determined not to let things go, ie smoking, and enjoy the good days, forget the bad days.

What this illness and its challenges has given me is to be more grateful for all that we have – a good family, a good home and, hopefully, a good future. I am now even more aware of other people's difficulties and how they cope. Through some of our lowest times I have been unable to see a way out, however, I now see a huge bright light at the end of this tunnel. We have learnt how best to deal with depression, he has learnt so much, so many coping strategies and this shows. Whilst we accept there will be setbacks, as a family we are looking forward to a bright future, an exciting future.

The quiet private man Steve was has opened up so much, communicating more, being able to discuss depression, how he is beating depression and now by helping others. I feel we have a lot of fun now, chatting, mixing with others, almost as if I am showing him off now. People are getting to know the real Steve. I think he is so intelligent, always has been but he has hidden this behind a mask and a façade but no longer. I have even had compliments from him, which of course I welcome, because I know they are genuine. I still feel, however, completely unable to speak my mind at times but this is my problem. It is that old fear of causing his depression and, therefore, I avoid an argument, but I am working on overcoming this.

I feel we both need to accept that at times there might be an argument or a disagreement but we both need to move on quickly afterwards in a positive way. As I am writing this I am remembering that historically I have seen our differences of opinions leading to arguments that would hang around for days and even weeks and I would be feeling that I had caused the depression. I tried my best to avoid these situations and at times say nothing, just stew. I recognise that to some extent this is my problem and I need to work on it just as much as he does.

I feel so lucky that we are coming through this and have so much to look forward to and that he is changing for the better and getting rid of the damned black dog.

But do not change too much, darling!!

The Story of Mrs Williams, Porthleven, Cornwall

My depression started after the death of our son, Vaughan, who died tragically in 1977 at the age of 17 years old from cystic fibrosis. John, my husband, and I were told from the outset of Vaughan's birth that he had the condition and rather matter-of-factly that he would not survive beyond his teen years. If this was not bad enough on its own, John and I were warned that we were both carriers of cystic fibrosis and that any future children ran the risk of being diagnosed with it as well. A double tragedy.

We did our best to raise Vaughan as normally as possible but because his physical development was impaired he was always smaller than the other children, which led to problems of bullying at times. Mentally, he was very bright and sharp and had the same stubborn streak as his father. Vaughan even managed to pass his driving test but even that led to problems as people would openly challenge him as to whether or not he was old enough to drive the car, which hurt him, and us, deeply.

Eventually, he passed away and his father, John, was deeply traumatised. Vaughan had idolised his father, to him he was god-like and John equally idolised Vaughan. After the death John was never the same; he withdrew into himself, like a clam closing its shell and never letting anyone in. John and I drifted apart, both emotionally and sexually, but we remained as a married couple. As I have mentioned before, John had a stubborn side to him, which to some extent carried him through those difficult years but at the same time made life hard for us both.

Looking back now, I know that my depression started when Vaughan passed away but I was not actually aware that it was actually depression. I merely thought that those periods were part of the 'normal' grieving process and that I was understandably sad at the loss of our only son. Because of this lack of knowledge I never sought assistance from anyone, never consulted with my doctor and never took any drugs or had any therapy or counselling. During this time, however, I took to drink to try and lift me out of my depressed state. Initially, drink helped me; it gave me a boost and induced a more positive frame of mind. But the effect was short-lived and after a while I would come tumbling back down, lower than where I was before the drink. This inevitably led me to drink more as I strived to stay out of the depressed state and eventually I had to drink more and more to get the same effect.

John would confront me about my drinking but I would deny it even though it was clear from the smell of alcohol on my breath that I had been drinking. This led to arguments between us, which in the end led to me agreeing to go to Alcoholics Anonymous to seek help. I went to several branches of the AA over the years but found the Falmouth centre the best; the other participants were always so warm and friendly. I was really surprised at the depth and breadth of the population represented at the meetings; they came from all walks of life and were aged from teenagers up to old age pensioners. I now no longer drink to escape my depression but it was a tough journey.

These periods of what I now know to be depression came and went during the intervening years between Vaughan's passing and John having a stroke several years ago. I came home to find John lying down and just by looking at him I knew he had had a stroke. One side of his face and body was contorted and looked so completely different. John never fully recovered from the stroke and I was left to care for him, which was very difficult for me. Eventually, I had to enlist the help of care staff as my depression worsened and I felt I could no longer cope with the world in general, let alone looking after John. I became so bad that I was admitted to the Longreach centre, where I stayed for a couple of days to get some rest and medication. The doctor there told me that the situation at home was certainly not helping but what could I do?

Looking back now, it would have been better for John, and me, had the stroke killed him outright. The quality of life that John had was pitiful and it was painful for me to watch and stand by. Here was the man I had loved from our schooldays and married, the only man I had ever been with, just wasting away in front of my eyes and it made me so sad. No wonder my depression had got worse.

In April 2007, John eventually passed away and was buried on top of his beloved son, Vaughan – together again at last. My depression continued as I grieved the loss of my husband and I sought bereavement counselling to help me with coming to terms with being alone and missing my husband. With due respect to my counsellor, though, I have not really had much benefit from our sessions. I find it difficult to get over the past and talk about old and very painful memories. I still continue to have the sessions, nonetheless; maybe there will be a breakthrough sometime.

When John passed away, I was left with many things to sort out, such as banks, other finances, the will, etc, that was both costly and demanding personally and I felt the effect in my depression. At times it was like I was continuously walking in treacle – as soon as I got one foot free the other would get stuck, a perpetual struggle. I always looked on the negative side of things; my glass would always be half empty in contrast to John whose glass was always half full. Even the slightest thing, such as light bulb going, was a major thing for me; it was a though I had no control over any of the events of my life and I was always being dealt a bad hand. I liken my depression to being in a dark hole with the proverbial black dog on my shoulder for company.

At night, despite going off to sleep easily enough, I would always awaken after a couple of hours, usefully feeling extremely anxious and tense about the most trivial matters. My whole body would be racked with tautness and I could not relax again until I got up, had a cigarette and made myself a hot drink. After a while I would go back to bed again, sleep for another couple of hours and the whole process would start over again. Going to bed at night was not something I looked forward to.

I have been taking Seroxat now for about three weeks, having changed recently from Citamopril, as Seroxat is supposed to help with anxiety. It's a bit too early to say if it's working but I am concerned about a report I read recently in a Sunday newspaper that named and shamed a number of anti-depressants, including Seroxat, in cases where suicide is being linked with the taking of these drugs.

I am writing this account from my bed as I'm currently recovering from a broken hip caused by a fall when walking my dog early one morning. I find that, like now, when I have something to focus on, ie getting better physically, it takes my mind off my depression. When there are no distractions or areas of particular attention then the black dog sits on my shoulder. It's painful to look back over my life and to see the course of events that have been played out over the years and I sometimes wish I had been dealt a better hand, but it is what it is and you just have to get on with it, black dog or no black dog.

The Story of Mark,
Falmouth, Cornwall

Today, I have my own business in Falmouth, which I run jointly with my partner, Susie. We bought the business in August 2007 and we are working really hard to make a success of it. It wasn't always like this, however, and it all could have ended so tragically the night I tried to take my life with a cocktail of sleeping tablets, paracetamol and alcohol the day before my birthday a number of years ago.

My journey did not start or end here but it was a significant event with my battle with depression. It all started many years before, growing up in London with my mum and dad and an elder brother. I remember like it was yesterday the acrimonious splitting up of my parents, the heated arguments and rows they used to constantly have. Because they spent most of their time trying to sort out their own problems, their marriage and ultimately their divorce, they had little time for me. Directly, or indirectly, I'm not really sure, but I got into a culture of drinking and recreational drugs at quite an early age, around 14 or 15. When my father eventually left home there was no fatherly figure to provide guidance, advice or even discipline and I was relatively free to choose my own lifestyle. I left school early with no qualifications and drifted in and out of jobs. I remember having a bad motorcycle accident when I was 16, which left me with a bad shoulder and arm and this restricted my ability to get some jobs. This was a problem for me in that my salary would invariably pay for my drink and drugs.

It was around this time that I began to suffer serious sexual abuse from three men. The first was a close friend of the family; he was, in fact, raised by my parents in the children's home they ran before I was born. This abuse was to last until I was 20 years old and even occurred in his home while his wife was asleep in the next bedroom. I am rather confused about this abuse emotionally and I am unable to understand why I would keep going back to this man while he was doing me harm. I do understand from his perspective that there was an issue around control, specifically controlling me, albeit it was perverted. Then, and even today, I feel like a child when I am around him and he is still in control. To this day, nobody in my family is aware of what I went through in the hands of this man; I rather think it is better to let sleeping dogs lie. I don't want to cause problems within the family and, more importantly, I'd rather that people just did not know what I had to endure.

I now try to avoid him as much as possible although a recent birthday party in London did bring us together again for the first time in a long time. I spent the whole occasion trying to avoid him while he seemed to be spending all his time trying to make contact with me. I had dreaded going to the celebration beforehand and my fears were justified; it was a completely harrowing experience, bringing terrible, chilling memories flooding back and reducing me to feel like a child again.

I liked to go swimming often and in those days there used to be swimming pool attendants and one, in particular, used to offer me the luxury of his personal changing room, complete with hot bath and clean towels. For this favour, though, he would invite himself into the room and fondle me sexually whilst I was soaking in the bathtub. Due to my previous sexual experience and the naivety of my age, I was confused about whether what was happening to me was right or wrong but I continued to swap the pleasure of a hot bath and my own changing room for the attendant's sexual gratification.

Then, while I was high on drink and drugs, I was raped twice by the same man, although my memory of the exact details is rather sketchy and, in any case, I would rather not make too much effort to recall these events.

I have often wondered why I never refused these sexual advances or experiences. Does this mean that in fact I consented; that it is not, therefore, abuse but a willing act? I honestly do not know why. I cannot change what has happened but I am trying to change how I feel about what happened and move on in my life. Although I am unclear about when my depression started or what caused it, if it is actually 'caused', these events have played a role in my future development and relationships.

I found work on the London Underground where I stayed for a number of years but all the while I was drinking heavily and using drugs constantly and this was playing a major role in my life. I moved to Falmouth in 1986 after visiting on holiday and falling in love with the place, particularly the culture of drinking and free availability of drugs. In addition, it was near the sea and the pace of life was much slower than that of London and this suited me right down to the ground.

I started a relationship and my partner and I bought a small apartment together. Unfortunately, we frequently rowed and argued, mostly about my excessive drinking and drug taking. Despite this, she fell pregnant and our daughter was born in 1990. During this time I was changing, almost without my noticing. I was becoming very tense, angry, morose and sullen and routinely withdrew into myself. My idea of escaping from these moods was to go down the pub, have a few drinks and chat about nothing to anyone who would listen. This only helped to fuel the breakdown in our relationship and, despite having a daughter together, our bond was not built on trust and a solid foundation and eventually we grew apart and she left, taking our daughter with her.

I started work for the NHS in 1991, working on a unit for adults with mental health problems and learning difficulties. Quite often the patients would become violent and I found the work both tiring physically and stressful mentally. Eventually, I decided to go to see my doctor about how I was feeling and he diagnosed depression. I did not know a great deal about the condition other than what I had learnt at work and was very surprised at this verdict. The doctor prescribed Prozac, which I started taking and at the same time cut down on my drinking and recreational drug taking. I found, ironically, Prozac to be a harsh drug to take in the sense that rather than calming me down, it actually stimulated me, so much so that the tenseness and anger I had before taking the drug was now enhanced.

At times, cooped up in my small apartment, I felt as if I could run up the walls, every muscle seemed tight and taut. It was at this point I decided that life was no longer worth living and I could no longer go on like this and I needed to end it all. I had some sleeping tablets already and I went to a chemist and bought loads of paracetamol. That night, after drinking heavily, I took the cocktail of drugs and washed them down with milk, went to bed and hoped I would never wake up again. This was the day before my birthday.

The next morning my new partner, Debbie, came around to my apartment and found me unconscious. She immediately called the ambulance and I was admitted to hospital where they tried to flush the drugs out of my system. When eventually I regained consciousness several days later my initial reaction was one of complete dejection that I was still alive. I could not even take my own life and this reinforced the low opinion I had of myself. What a failure!

After coming out of hospital, I went back to heavy drinking and drug taking, although I was still taking Prozac, and I was still tense and angry all the time. During a drunken argument with Debbie I uncharacteristically became violent and hit her, causing her nose to bleed. The police were called and I was arrested and spent the night in Camborne police station to cool off and sober up. I was ultimately convicted of common assault, which I am extremely ashamed of. I had never before become violent and believe that Prozac had played a part in changing my personality, which has left me feeling very bitter towards the manufacturer. Here I was taking a prescribed drug that should have made me feel better but in fact was making me feel worse.

I was fortunate during these difficult times that my employer, the NHS, was very supportive and understanding and this was a huge relief for me. Had they not been this way I would have lost my job and this would only have served to compound my problems.

After the violent incident I went back to my doctor and they agreed to change my medication from Prozac to another anti-depressant, the name of which I cannot remember. This had the effect of reducing the tenseness and anger to a degree but my feeling of depression remained, albeit at a lower level. Fortunately, Debbie and I stayed together despite my assault. She fell pregnant even though she was on the Pill and I took precautions. However, we both had the view the time was not right for us, as our relationship was still not as strong as it could be and we reluctantly decided on an abortion. This affected us both emotionally, but more so with Debbie.

In 1996, Debbie fell accidentally pregnant again but this time we decided to keep the baby and she gave birth to a little girl, my second daughter. Our relationship, though, was still stormy and prone to ups and downs on a regular basis. The death of Debbie's mum not long after was a real blow for her and, to some extent, compounded the problems that existed between us as she needed space to grieve and a partner who could offer support, which I did not do very well. Painfully, we decided to go our separate ways and for the second time a daughter of mine left me to live with her mum. Initially, I was devastated at the breakdown in our relationship and the resultant split but I knew it was the right thing for both of us. Gradually, my mood improved and, in conjunction with my doctor, we agreed to reduce the dosage and dependency on anti-depressants. I wanted to feel real again, without the artificial haze created by the drugs. At the same time I had consciously chosen to reduce my intake of drink and recreational drugs. This was a real challenge for me, considering the length of time and enjoyment I had got from them. Maybe when I was drinking and taking drugs I did not remember or dwell on events in my past, but they were doing me no good and I had to find others ways of dealing with what had happened all those years ago.

On top of all this, my work in the NHS continued to be stressful and tiring, with violence by patients a regular occurrence. In addition, there was talk of the unit closing down and the threat of redundancy. I felt the pressure of this uncertain future too much and I went sick from work due to high levels of anxiety, worry and stress. I had been working there for 17 years and relied on the job for income and security. Although I was on sick leave, I am reluctant to say that I was depressed; I had stopped taking anti-depressants some time before. I like to think I was able to manage myself and my moods better, and I felt able to distinguish between stress and anxiety and full-blown depression.

It was during this time that I met Susie and we started going out together. My efforts at reducing both my drinking and drug taking had succeeded to an extent I no longer drank to excess regularly and restricted drug taking to special events or occasions. This undoubtedly helped me both in the relationship with Susie and in dealing with the uncertainties at work.

In July 2007 I was paid off by the NHS and Susie and I decided to invest in a small business together. The pay-off was used to put the deposit down on the business and although we have got off to a slow start, we are putting all our efforts into getting it going. Both of us have an aversion to winter, with Susie especially prone to Seasonal Affective Disorder (SAD), and I have contemplated going back to the doctor to discuss this with them but I am reluctant to be prescribed anti-depressants again. I would rather feel that I can manage this low mood myself by doing things that give me a lift, such as walking, listening to music, swimming and, of course, spending time with my two lovely daughters. I still enjoy a drink and it does help me to relax and unwind but in complete moderation.

Although I am attempting to manage my depression I do feel it will be with me for a long time. My low moods appear very gradually, so much so that they seem to creep up on me before I realise it, but helpfully, Susie can usually spot it before I do. Over the years I have seen many counsellors, therapists and occupational health specialists but I never felt that I benefited from the sessions. Because of my past I was reluctant to talk about some of my experiences, which at the time I preferred to keep confidential. To this day my mum is still unaware of the abuse I suffered at the hands of the men in my teens, particularly the close associate of the family. I did, however, have a really good doctor at one stage who was very interested into looking at the causes of my depression and I did share the details of my unwanted sexual experiences with them. This led to a solicitor becoming involved as well as the police. A claim was made on my behalf to the Criminal Injuries Compensation Board but was unsuccessful. No matter, I now look back on the past as the past and I now concentrate on the present and the future. Whatever the cause of my depression – trauma, drink, drugs, stress, anxiety, seasons or indeed any combination of these – I will continue to attempt to control the symptoms and live my life as I choose to. Perversely, the unsuccessful attempt on my life was the turning point in my journey and it made me realise I had responsibilities, not just for myself but for my two daughters as well.

The Story of David,
Plymouth, Devon

Looking back on my life in retrospect, I now believe my depression started from the moment I came into this world. I was born a boy but my mother desperately wanted a sister for her 10-year-old son. Although I was far too young to realise it, subconsciously I was neither loved nor nurtured as a young baby should have been by their mother from birth. You may find this an extraordinary statement to make but I believe it to be true. Indeed, my mother gave me to her sister to look after for six weeks and I am mindful deep down that she did give me love and affection; you just know when bonds are created at these young ages by moments of touch and tenderness. I do know that my mum was abused as a child and maybe this was the cause of some of her behaviour towards me.

I do not know, but maybe my mother had depression after I was born, either caused by a post-natal reaction or by the fact that she was disappointed at my sex; or maybe even a combination of the both of them. All through my childhood years the overriding memory is one of being unwanted and unloved. I remember even as a child feeling real anger and resentment towards my mum and I have carried these hurtful feelings around with me for over 35 years. My engineer father was like an outsider looking in, not really taking an active part in the family unit, most certainly not from my perspective. He probably felt excluded because my mum really only showed any affection and love towards my eldest brother. My father liked to drink and when he had had enough booze he became very sarcastic, to the point of being caustic with his remarks and, when he was like this, I would get really scared at the way he looked at me.

I remember a time when my brother made a roast dinner and

put too much salt on the potatoes. Our father made us all eat them, even though they were really inedible, just to prove that my brother had tried and that he was trying to impress my mother that he did care for him. My eldest brother, when he became old enough, became my carer, taking the place of both my mother and my father. I grew up isolated mentally and emotionally from the rest of the family and felt rejected, feelings that I have always carried round with me. This became compounded when my mother died when I was 14 from cancer. I think I was also angry with her for dying when I was so young. Looking back, I really believe that parents should be allowed to say that they do not love their children or a child, but our society does not understand this nor expect it. In other's eyes it should be natural for a mother to feel a maternal bond for their offspring but had she been allowed to say she did not love me maybe I could have thought and reacted differently, maybe I could have accepted this and moved on. I do not really know.

I had a younger sister whom I would constantly hit and chase around the house, initially without any chastisement, which encouraged me to do it even more. Eventually my father could take this no longer and told me off, saying that I should be ashamed of myself. I did indeed feel shame after this and I have carried this shame around for years, so much so that I could not even face my sister when I visited her in America many years later. Why had I teased and bullied my sister like this? I can only speculate that it was attention I was seeking and the more I did it without getting my needs satisfied the more I felt compelled to act to force my father's hand.

When I was 11 I fractured my skull at school and ended up in hospital. I was looked after by two lovely nurses who gave me love and affection aplenty, something of an uncommon gift. When I eventually recovered and was well enough to go home I immediately felt unloved and unwanted again and thoughts of deliberately fracturing my skull or causing some other injury to myself came into my head just so I could have an excuse to go back to hospital and be properly and tenderly cared for by soft and gentle women.

Even as a teenager I kept myself to myself and isolated from others. I used to like dark winter nights when I could draw the curtains and pull up the blankets and feel all cosy in my room by myself. I went to school but felt like I was never educated. I could not communicate with my peers or the teachers, neither of whom could really connect with this rather strange, quiet lad who sat at the back of the class and just didn't participate. It is hard to imagine how I actually learnt to read and write.

Isolation. The very word conjures up the feeling of loneliness, being alone and without relation to others, even quarantine. This is what I chose, this is what I knew, this is what life was for me. To know one is missing something one must first have experienced it and developed a taste for it. I developed a deep sensitivity to criticism, even slight or perceived criticism. If people criticised me, real or imaginary, this meant that they did not like or accept me and this nourished my desire to be on my own. If you are not around others they cannot criticise you and you will, therefore, not feel rejected or not liked.

At the age of 21 I left home and moved to Birmingham but quickly moved to London where I had no money and nowhere to stay. I met a man who offered me digs and we went back to his place. Knowing I had no money he gave me ten shillings, and although I had never had experience with homosexuality, I instinctively knew that there were sexual motives attached to the favours of money and a room. Not wanting to have any part of this I left hurriedly and slept in a doss-house that night, which was a really unpleasant experience. I decided after this that London really was not the place to be after all; how can one be alone in such a big city?

I made my way to North Wales where my father had a small cottage. This was ideal, I could tuck myself away here and not be bothered by anyone, and I could isolate myself mentally and physically. However, unbeknown to me, depression crept silently upon me and was starting to affect my whole well-being. A neighbour became concerned with me staying in the cottage by myself and contacted my father. My brother came to collect me, not my father, and took me back home and booked an appointment for me to see a doctor. He diagnosed a mental breakdown and sent me to a mental hospital. My reaction to this was 'thank God', hopefully they could make me better. At the time electro convulsive therapy (ECT) was the favoured treatment for mental health problems and I had to persuade the doctors that this was what I needed. In the end they conceded and I had three ECT treatments, which did absolutely nothing for me. They subsequently deemed that I was cured and there was nothing more wrong with me and they discharged me.

I then briefly worked in a hotel and saved enough money to put down a deposit on a small farm in Wales producing milk. Despite my depression I could always find work and function at some level. I managed to do this for several years until I decided I wanted to sell ice-cream! Again, without knowing it, my depression was sneaking up on me and creating irrational thoughts – why on earth ice-cream? Anyway, I sold the farm and went off to sell ice-cream but my depression was worsening all the time. I was slipping down into a deep black hole from which I could see no return; the sides were too steep to climb and, in any case, I had neither the will nor the inclination to do so anyway. When you are in that hole there is no way out. Eventually, the depression became so bad that I had to end the constant misery by opting to take my own life. I bought a lot of paracetamol tablets and took the lot, wishing to end my infernal suffering once and for all.

Destiny took a hand here at this point and my quest for release from suffering was denied. I survived the attempted suicide but was left with damage to my liver, meaning that I have to watch what I eat and drink. My brother, again, came and collected me and convinced me to go into business with him, which I did, and I eventually managed to buy a house. This did not last long though and I sold the house to go travelling around the country. I literally 'chased' number plates to different parts of the UK. Why I do not know, but I was in a high state of mania at the time and thoughts were barely rational at these times. I managed to get arrested for a traffic offence and sent to Wakefield hospital for mental observation but released. I was arrested in London for causing a crash by going through red lights. I was almost out of control.

But the mania was to end and I fell back into that black hole again, having a second breakdown in the process but at least I avoided attempting suicide this time. I then moved to Plymouth in an effort to sort myself out. I bought a fish and chip shop and ran this successfully for about three years. I decided to sell this business and bought another fish and chip shop in a different area of Plymouth and eventually sold this as well. Rather bizarrely, I was talked into buying a night club on Plymouth's infamous Union Street. However, whilst having the club my depression returned with a vengeance, getting progressively worse and worse. The problem was that the condition would degenerate without me realising it; it was so gradual that I never realised how low I had got until I was at the bottom of the damned hole.

At the time of buying the club I thought this would never work, this just wasn't me. How could an isolationist buy and run an establishment designed to bring crowds of people together to socialise and enjoy themselves? Last it did, for ten years in fact, but like everything else I had done, there was an expiry date on the venture and I sold the club onto someone else. At this time I was again in a high state of mania and had serious delusions of grandeur. Having sold the club, my pockets were awash with money and I spent, spent and spent. I bought gold watches, rings, bracelets, necklaces, you name it. I went travelling by train all over the place. London, Penzance, everywhere spending. I drank coffee after coffee after coffee, sending me on an artificial high with all that caffeine, maybe trying to bring myself out of my depression.

With most of my money gone I eventually came back to Plymouth, where I had a house, but soon got into trouble. I deliberately scratched a neighbour's car, for reasons I am not clear about apart from the fact that I saw him as a threat. A threat against what or whom I do not know but I did it none the less. I was questioned by the police and, in due course, admitted that I had done it. After checking my records of time in mental institutions they gave me the option of either prison or Moorhaven, a mental hospital on the outskirts of Plymouth. Here I was given an assessment prior to going to court where the judge decided to fine me and confine me to Moorhaven.

It was during my time here that I asked to see a Catholic priest to see if I could discover God and ask for his support. For whatever reason, I could not find him and abandoned this idea, preferring to engage with spirituality rather than religion. In Moorhaven they prescribed various drugs for me to help with my depression but despite these I had my third breakdown and found myself once again in that deep and dark pit sitting by myself at the bottom. The medication brought on sudden blackouts but for some reason the doctors thought I was 'swinging the lead' and putting it all on just to stay in the comfort of the hospital. Eventually, I was basically asked to leave on the basis they could find nothing wrong with me.

So I left Moorhaven and since then have taken no more medication (no more blackouts either). When I came out I spent a spell living with a friend's girlfriend until I got sorted out. This friend tried to persuade me to sell my house but others said no, that I should hang onto it as security. I was confused – why would he want me to sell up? Maybe he wanted some of my money, I'm not sure. Anyway, I kept the house and signed on the dole, a far cry from a night club owner!

I started to go to the spiritualist church and I had a relationship with a woman but that did not last too long, probably because of me and my behaviour. I was beginning to isolate myself again and became afraid to go outside the front door of my house because of what I had done to my neighbour's car. Somehow I had to overcome these fears and my self-imposed isolation if I was to get back into work and have a purpose to continue with life. I did manage to get three part-time jobs – one as a debt-collector, one as a sales representative for a credit company, rather perversely, and the last as a care-assistant looking after the personal needs of disadvantaged people. This last job I quite liked and was able to increase the number of hours I was working to the point that I could give up the other two jobs, which I was glad about. Today, I am still looking after people with needs, particularly adults with learning difficulties, and find the work quite rewarding.

At the time of taking the job I really did not think that I would truly be able to help others, particularly given my background and track record, but I liked and respected the person who had interviewed me and I find it so hard to say no to someone I like. However, having spent some time doing this work I can honestly say that it has brought about a real breakthrough in my personal journey through life in the shape and recognition of the fact I was now receiving, for the first time in my life, unconditional love. This was given to me by one of the adults I was caring for and who was staying with me at my house during his time on the programme. I had never before experienced unconditional love, I never even knew it existed until this point and the realisation that I had been missing out on this key emotion all my life left me feeling rather sad and, quite frankly, somewhat depressed. Why did I have to discover it so late in my life, when I was nearly 50? Why, why, why had I not had this as a child, teenager, or a young adult? I'm not blaming my mother – things were what they were – but I cannot help wondering if I had had love, affection and a physical connection with her during my early formative years, how might I have turned out? Who knows!

Working with adults with learning difficulties has been the biggest salvation of my life and provided me with my purpose in life. They say you get back what you give out and this has most certainly been true for me during these years of caring for others. Whilst the depression is always there, it can be managed if you can get outside of your own thoughts and be active doing other things. I read lots of self-help books, not to look back and dwell on the past in order to analyse everything but to look forward and take positive action, to learn new coping mechanisms and strategies and to clarify why I am like I am. One of my biggest challenges is communication with others. I just do not do small talk! Books are good but they cannot be a substitute for the real thing of social interaction with other human beings. After years of self-imposed, habitual isolationism I never did learn the art of engaging in idle chitter-chatter but I remind myself that I still have time to learn, there is always time to learn.

Over time I have learnt that I can control my mood by adjusting my diet and specifically by avoiding foods high in sugar content, which tend to put me into low moods. I also enjoy films that have themes of hope and courage and that have positive endings, as this is exactly what they give me. I also find that by exercising regularly each morning, either at home or by walking, helps to raise my spirits, sometimes even at the expense of exhausting myself; it is a satisfied feeling of tiredness. Another pastime that helps lift my spirits is reading light-hearted fiction books and listening to the radio; these help me to escape from my inner thoughts and to be more present in the real world. I love and admire heroes, either in film or in books, as these represent role models for me of what I would like to have been or become and also because they fight evil and defend the good, just like I battle depression but I have yet to achieve hero status as I have not yet won.

One aspect of depression that I find confusing and, as yet, have still to find a satisfactory answer to is the fact that I can go to bed at night in a good or even very good mood but wake up in low mood. What is happening to me and my body when I am asleep? What is happening in my mind or to my chemical balance during sleep that affects my mood? If I knew the answer to this, would this be the key to my depression and that of others? My depressed world is an unreal world of dark places, confused thoughts and unhealthy, useless thoughts – who wants to voluntarily be in this place? Far better to do things that are useful and helpful and which put you in touch with the rest of humanity and relative positivity. Drugs, to me, only address the symptoms but do not address the core issues and I, therefore, do not take any and have not done so for a long time. I have learnt not to trust doctors, I trust only myself to work on me and bring about meaningful change in how I view and act in my world.

The Story of Lorraine, Plymouth, Devon

Depression: How it Was for Me

It is hard to know when it started; it creeps up on you and cloaks you in its mist until eventually you find that you cannot think clearly and you carry the black cloud around with you. It could have started as long ago as adolescence, bullied by other girls and always with low self-esteem.

Years passed by and even with my adventurous spirit and strong willpower I took the mist with me.

On the surface I coped well with the loss of my strong and powerful beloved dad, a miscarriage, the breakdown of my marriage, and loss of my younger sister. I continued to function and soldiered on bringing up my son alone. Without realising it the cloud thickened as I eventually became anxious and afraid of everyday things. I can remember being afraid to go out; I imagined someone would break into my home and steal my most treasured possessions (things that are worth nothing to a burglar). I hadn't realised this was depression, I thought it was life. I would have bad weeks and some good days. The good days were blue sky days, as usually the sun was shining and it was indeed a beautiful blue sky. The bad weeks were a black tunnel with the hint of a light some way off. From time to time someone would come along the tunnel with a torch and rescue me for a while; although short-lived, it would bring me a little closer to the light. My doctor recognised the symptoms immediately and over the years I had several long courses of Prozac.

She felt that I had a chemical imbalance probably from post-natal depression, which had continued with my monthly menstrual cycle.

My mum was my closest ally and helped me the best she could; she would know when I was at my lowest ebb and have my son to stay with her; she would write me notes of encouragement or leave flowers for me in my flat. Friends would avoid me when I was 'there' and I got used to that.

People who are not depressed can spot your weakness, your vulnerability, and sometimes take advantage – something that only becomes apparent in retrospect.

Eventually I understood that only I could rescue myself with professional help and a different way of thinking. I no longer feel a victim; I am queen of my own world. I learnt about myself, my fears, beliefs; rediscovered buried dreams and set about finding a way to make them happen.

This has taken several years and I am still learning in my constant endeavour to get my own needs met assertively, to believe in and love myself, to remain positive. It's very easy to slip back into old ways and thought processes. Now when I feel the cool mist of anxiety creeping around me I know to look for what is not working, what is the cause. Keeping physically fit is important too; nothing over the top; something that fits my lifestyle. At the moment I walk, swim and I am learning to dance. The adage healthy body, healthy mind seems to work in reverse – healthy mind, healthy body. Friends and family have embraced the changes in me and my new lifestyle.

The Story of Lynda, Newquay, Cornwall

One of the causes of my depression at that time was how alienated I felt living in England as a foreigner in a strange land. This is my personal experience which I think is of some importance to the understanding of depression in our society, especially today when as a civilization we are moving around the globe at an alarming rate and relocating to lands not of our birth and how it affects each one of us.

My mother was born in the UK, so I and my daughter were allowed an ancestral visa entry into the UK to work for four years without a work permit. In 2001 I won two Virgin airline tickets to London in an office competition and at the end of 2001 I was made redundant due to a merger of the company I was working for. My daughter had already been living in London for a year, so it was almost an automatic decision to leave South Africa and move to the UK. For no other reason did I leave South Africa and I also had no intention of staying in the UK. It was just going to be the four years to make a lot of money and go back home again. Of course, with hindsight, I can now see where things went wrong for me.

I had already made contact with a reputable recruitment agency in London for my arrival and I had a rather impressive CV. Working as a corporate secretary in Johannesburg for a French merchant bank I had met and arranged dealings with numerous presidents of companies and countries in my line of work, so I was quite confident I would find a good position in London. Little did I know I was about to meet my first culture shock. I would say I am a typical example of a 'loud, in-your-face' South African, with great enthusiasm and wide-eyed expectation, fast and efficient. But I didn't seem to secure the interviews I was sent to, and now I know why. The British are a very reserved, restrained and conservative type and my boisterous demeanour was perceived as not professional. I never managed to break into 'the City' and ended up on the 'High Street', as they call it. Nonetheless, throughout my dealings with my office colleagues, most of them being British, I was constantly at odds with my surroundings and increasingly I began to feel alienated from them. I was not included or felt welcomed and as I was later told "odd" and "strange". I had never encountered this behaviour before in my entire life. I could not understand why it should be so different. I've always been included and have never been alone. So I began to think and, therefore, believe, that I must be a bad person because no one liked me and latterly because I am South African. I never thought that I might be a bad person because I never had reason to think so. No-one had ever indicated that to me, not even my ex-husband. Now I was looking at myself differently. Consequently the situations became worse and I withdrew more and more, never making one friend, not one in seven years! My only consolation was that my bosses liked me because I worked well, was reliable and efficient, and I was proud of that, but it didn't make me any more likable among my colleagues.

Because I was now negatively charged, everything else began to look bad and bleak. The English cold and grey weather for months on end began to get to me chronically. I couldn't afford to rent a place of my own in exorbitant London, so was living in a room in a house share. My four walls became my prison. Mandela became my hero and my inspiration to endure (and I had met him a few times in SA).

And then my father died suddenly of a heart attack. From then on it was downhill fast. Because he was all I had left in my life, he was my lifeline to going home to South Africa. And now he was gone, and I felt my life had too. Now I was even more alone in a world I felt didn't like me. I have no other family, my mother and older brothers having died many years previously. My brothers never married. I had been divorced 10 years before and had no contact with my ex-family. I also had no living aunties or uncles or grandparents. I had no one to talk to, not even my daughter who by now was also feeling the same as me – alienated and alone. She too was depressed. I went to see my counsellor at the local health centre to be able to talk to someone at least. I at first refused anti-depressants because I felt my situation was circumstantial and not of a chemical imbalance in my brain.

To try to meet other South Africans, I started working weekends at a South African food shop. The other girls were all in their 20s, not that I minded that, and the South Africans in my age group, who came into the shop to buy stuff from home, came with their families and girlfriends. So no go there. I joined a group of South African woman my age and we met in a pub once a month, but I could not identify with them either as they talked about their families and homes and high-paying jobs, all of which I didn't have to talk about. So no go there. I joined a camera club, a volunteer group, a book club, Open University and studied English law and social science. Even a dinner club where we met once a month. Still I felt the odd one out. Internet dating was a joke, even a South African site for Saffas in London. The majority were youngsters. I still went home alone. Not even my own community had a place for me.

I continued like this for more than a year until I couldn't take the constant tears. I felt I was at my own everlasting funeral. So I asked to see a psychiatrist and I requested a South African one too, so that she could somehow identify with my feelings of alienation. She put me on anti-depressants, Venlafaxine eventually, 37.5mg at first, going up to 75mg. Paroxetine and Sertraline gave me an upset tummy. I can't say that they were of any help to me, or the psychiatrist for that matter, because it was my situation that changed around the same time I was on the anti-depressants.

A young family member of one of my daughter's friends from South Africa, who was living in London, and I became friends after his wife left him. We spent a lot of time together and I felt elated. I could be of help to someone else and he filled up my lonely hours. I had something else to think about and it helped me a lot.

My daughter worked through her depression by going to see a

counsellor at the local health centre but she never took anti-depressants. We are very close and we were in support of one another just by understanding each other's situation, but both feeling quite powerless to help one another in the situation.

I moved out of London after living there for seven years. The claustrophobia and isolation of a city made my situation worse and I felt I would kill if I didn't get out of there. My daughter left London a year previously and moved to Newquay. We both now share a lovely flat together and both work minimum wage, but are definitely both happier. The people are friendlier and they at least greet you in the street.

I still feel alone as a South African living in England, shocked by the verbal abuse I received after England lost to SA in the rugby World Cup this year. Still trying to fit in this world I find myself in, I went to an evening for South Africans in Newquay but found only families huddled together. I bought myself a South African drink at the bar and approached two ladies my age and asked if I could join them. They were British and doctors!!! We chatted till I finished my drink and they commented that I was very brave. Brave but still alone. I have become a British citizen now, but I remain South African to my core.

I have been off anti-depressants for about two years now and never want to have them again. I did not like the dizzy sensation you have while slowly coming off them. And I don't want to be that depressed again. Those dark, dark thoughts that consume and anaesthetise you. It's all in your head. I know those thoughts so well, so I know when they come into my head and try to bring me down. As soon as it happens I negate them with positive thoughts, and I know in your deep depression, how extremely hard it is to find *any* positive thoughts at all. It's a constant battle to keep those thoughts away, but once you are aware of their destruction, you can begin to combat them with positivity. That's why I had to leave London. Here in Newquay I can take a walk to the beach and look and see and smell the sea and waves, and that's positive enough for me. Depression doesn't just go away, it's an exhausting mental battle. But you can win, really and truly, you can win.

The Story of Mrs S, Truro, Cornwall

I think it was in 1959 at Easter that my depression first hit me. I had been teaching in Ghana for roughly three months after staying in French West Africa five years to stop a Protestant school closing. My younger sister had replaced me there but for only one year, as I had been a nervous wreck after so much strain and overwork coupled with loneliness and nervous exhaustion. I drove in my car from Cape Coast with a colleague called Pat and my African cook/house boy. I began to feel so exhausted that Pat drove my car on to Ibadan in Nigeria, where we were due to stay with someone who had been at my London college with me and was teaching Latin at a girls' school.

I saw a doctor, who sent me to a specialist at the huge hospital in Ibadan, called the University College Hospital. He kept me in for four days over Easter, doing several tests, some under anaesthetic, but decided there was nothing wrong that rest could not put right. One doctor said that if I had been over-burdened emotionally, that would be quite sufficient to explain the weakness in my legs and the total lethargy I was experiencing.

Pat drove my car back to Ghana and I stayed resting with my friend in Ibadan, before flying back to Takoradi in Ghana, where the deputy head met me and drove me back to my bungalow at the school. My body had gone on strike, but at least I was able to help with the marking and had some girls down for English orals in my bungalow.

Gradually I got back to 8 hours teaching of exam groups, whilst attending hospital for injections. One doctor diagnosed lumbago, another neuritis and I had painful physiotherapy and heat treatment.

An aunt my parents had gone to live with died, so at least I no longer had the worry of trying to save money to buy them a house. Once I had covered the exam syllabus, I flew home early in June, booked into a Droitwich hotel for a complete rest and bought a cheap car. I could drive with no problems but could not walk for more than 100 yards. In London I saw a Harley Street specialist, but hardly had the strength to walk back to the underground. I rested a week in the Elizabeth Garrett Anderson Hospital before being transferred to a Barnet hospital. My problem was called nervous exhaustion, but I now know it was severe depression. A friend brought me embroidery to do, as I longed for something to do with my hands. Otherwise there was just radio and reading.

I flew home for good to Burton-on-Trent, where my parents had moved to share the home of my aunt, Millie, who had died before my arrival. I bought a cheap second-hand car, a VW Beetle, in which I took Mother shopping and would meet her at the bottom of a steep hill, when she came back by bus from an evening of bridge. Before I returned to England I had been interviewed by proxy in Kumasi, Ghana, by an acquaintance of the head of a school in Burton-on-Trent. I took the job but I particularly disliked the English head-master, who was something of a slave driver. One particularly difficult class locked me out of the library on one occasion. The stress was considerable, the school being divided into two buildings a quarter of a mile apart.

Burton was belching filthy smoke from dozens of chimneys and the foul smell of the Marmite factory near the school was nauseating. When I took the car, I always found it coated with filth and I seemed to have a cough and a cold much of the time. I had no friends nearer than London and the parental home was quite sordid. Their dirty habits, deafness and many eccentricities were most irritating. The weather in the Christmas holidays was appalling. We had a burst pipe and the Post Office was working to rule. With time to think, life seemed pretty intolerable and it took very little to make me weep from self-pity and loneliness. I was 36 and there was no eligible bachelor in sight.

By February, the old depression returned, triggered, I think, by influenza. I was forced to stay away from school, staying in bed with a painful back, one parent or the other bringing me meals. The doctor came twice, once for two minutes and then for three. When I managed to drive myself to his surgery, he muttered insensitive remarks about getting a grip on myself. He was always anxious to shut me up and obviously thought I was a hypochondriac, for he and his receptionist stood and watched me walk to the car. I was not entitled to sickness benefit as I had not made the 26 contributions missing in the year ending 1961. I was entitled to 23 days on full salary and 46 on half pay. A member of staff brought me marking to do and reports and I was able to send back suggestions for work for my stand-in.

I had an appointment with a psychiatrist, who said the physical effects of depression were very common but would not last long. I went for physiotherapy three times a week. My whole metabolism had slowed down. Above all I needed rest, but there was always school work, housework, and garden and church responsibilities. I felt in a cleft stick with tears of despair deep inside, where there was no glimmer of hope. Life was an endless desert. A sister said "Go for your own health. Give the old folk an ultimatum", but my mother only had another year or so to live and I was the only un-married one of her five children able to help. I had returned to Burton for her sake. I did not want to spoil her last years, but she was certainly difficult to live with. If only she would keep her hearing aid switched on! Various friends and other people offered their pet nos-trums in order to help me.

I started reading about psychiatry but my doctor disapproved, but what I read corresponded to my state: 'Depression is pathologi-cal, when frustration occurs in relation to some conscious but very much overvalued end, the depth of depression being proportionate to the degree of overvaluation. The overvaluation is derived from an exaggerated ego-ideal.' I also found there a list of all my symp-toms: 'headache, dyspepsia, lack of appetite, bad taste in the mouth, constipation, irritability – especially to noises (that terrible sucking noise dad made when he ate), lassitude, general weakness and ex-haustion, lack of concentration, disturbed, un-refreshing sleep and difficulty getting up in the morning'. The book said people recovered despite, rather than because of physical treatment they received.

I had a husband-shaped void that did not match anyone I knew. A minister I met said "Caution – long load" applied to the whole of life. It had many burdens in store and all we could do was live from day to day, asking for strength to bear the immediate pain and not worrying about the future.

After a spell of rest in a psychiatric hospital I managed to get through the summer term without falling ill again, but gave in my resignation without having another job to go to. I remained unemployed for a whole term. If I had not felt tied to the Burton area, there would have been no problem. I replied to an advertisement in the paper asking for a friend in her 30s with a view to marriage. Alex Simpson and I got on quite well when we met fairly often for two months. He came to lunch, but my mother thought him totally unsuitable. He was a charge-hand at Ind Coope's brewery and not in my class. We had a pleasant day out in London, but soon after he became cold, saying "We are not going to get on well, you will always be doing church work", which he did not approve of. His cousin had been warning him off marrying anyone religious. It was a bitter pill to swallow.

After many applications, I was offered a job at Hodge Hill Girls' Grammar School in Birmingham. It was a bitterly cold winter and my digs were freezing. I booked to attend evening classes every evening just to keep warm for an hour or so. A month after the start of the autumn term, I succumbed to the dreaded flu again. The physics master, who lived in Lichfield, would drive me all the way home to Burton, as I was feeling so groggy. For several days I could not eat. A long depression ensued.

After five weeks I went into St Matthews' hospital, Burntwood, where I had an X-ray and was put on a new drug called Allegron, which gradually made me feel better, though I could only stay up for a few hours a day. I was bursting into tears for trivial reasons. I stayed up for about six hours a day, did a lot of embroidery, helped with washing up and fetched bed pans for other patients. One young woman said she hated everyone and would like to live on a lighthouse. Another came in swearing like a trooper and threatened to walk home in her nightie. I was being pressurised to accept electric shock treatment, but I knew it affected memory and as I relied on that to earn a living, I firmly refused. I could see the effects in the vague ramblings of other patients. The boffins got impatient with me and said if I only wanted a rest, I could do that at home. I stayed there a month, but was far from fit when I left. My Burton GP told me to pull myself together and obviously thought I was a hypochondriac and malingerer. In Birmingham I found a much more sympathetic lady doctor who backed me up in refusing ECT. My drug was changed to Nardil, which made me sleepy all the time.

I got back to work only a fortnight before the end of term. I had been on half pay so I was thankful to get back on full salary before the holiday. One of my mother's sisters came to stay with a daughter and was still with us when my mum died. A doctor came at 11pm to give her something to help her sleep. I heard the ghastly death rattle at 4am. I had been given morphine tablets but was told that they would shorten her life. I wish now that I had given her the lot, but Doctor did not dare say I was free to do that. No animal would be allowed to suffer as much as she did in those last few months. A vicar came to lead a little service in our lounge before she was driven away in a black van, as she had bequeathed her body to the medical profession.

I had rows with my sister and when she said "Go back to the mental hospital". I threw water in her face. I managed to get a mortgage to buy a maisonette on the first floor of a house in Castle Bromwich for only £2650.

In July, Alex suddenly reappeared one Sunday, saying he wanted to ask for forgiveness for the churlish way he had behaved in sending me packing three years before. I was expecting to meet my former African fiancé, Robert, in London. He was strangely cold and explained he had made an African girl pregnant in Paris. I took him to the Lake District. He was due to marry the girl in Paris, so I bought him a pair of sheets and gave him an embroidered tablecloth I had made. I found it quite extraordinary that he would later write and say "nothing is changed between me and you".

A week later I got engaged to Alex. I knew I didn't love him, but a marriage of companionship in my 40s might be less intolerable than the lonely, desperately unhappy life I was stuck with. I went down with another dose of flu, which took a month to shake off, but at least this did not lead to depression. I married him at the end of the year, when I had precisely £23 in my account. No-one came from his family in Scotland, but we had 70 guests. Alex took a week off work and got a transfer to a brewery in Birmingham.

I became pregnant almost at once, and naturally feared post-natal depression, but it did not happen. I have had none since. My marriage to Alex lasted until he died of a stroke in 1975.

Robert's marriage ended when he'd had four children but I never saw him again.

The Story of Alan,
Plymouth, Devon

My Experience with Depression

When I was 37 my father died after a long period of ill health. The following year it was announced that the school where I had worked for most of my adult life was to close down, and all staff – my colleagues and friends – would be dispersed to other schools. In the run-down to this closure, long-standing but denied problems in my 15-year marriage surfaced and I left the relationship. The resulting reduction in my financial circumstances and move to a much smaller and less desirable home coincided with my redeployment to a large, tough inner-city school where I became very much the new boy.

I was far from happy but managing to cope with life. I found solace in a new relationship, which I entered far too soon with far too much hope and commitment – "loving not wisely but too well". When the relationship inevitably broke down, so did I. All the anxiety and uncertainty of the previous few years had been held at bay by staking my future on an exciting but uncertain relationship. Sadly it was based mainly on a lot of wishful thinking and when it failed all those anxieties and uncertainties seemed to crash in on me all at once. I felt massive surges of adrenalin and anxiety, and found myself unable to function or even think straight, pointlessly on the move like a wasp in a jar.

The day after the break-up I went to see my GP. When I opened my mouth to explain the situation I lost control and burst into tears. When eventually I was able to finish my sorry tale, he prescribed anti-depressants and counselling, both of which I was able to start at once.

The following three or four months seemed like a grey hole in my life. I got up each day, and although I was never suicidal it would have seemed a blessing to stay asleep and never have to wake up and face a day again. I went to work most days because I was too lonely and afraid to be on my own. I filled my diary with an endless succession of tasks and visits, none taking too long or demanding much commitment because I seemed to have the attention span of a gnat. I stopped listening to music because almost anything would reduce me to tears. Alcohol and tobacco, two of my routine pleasures, would plunge my mood immediately so I gave them up. Hunger or lack of sleep had the same effect. The only thing which improved my mood – or rather dulled my negative feelings – was the effect of the anti-depressants, which left me insulated from the world as if in a big glass jar.

Slowly, very slowly, things started to improve. The three or four months felt much longer than they actually were, but they did pass. Gradually I started to experience the occasional good day when my mood did not drop for at least a few hours. The interval between these days reduced until the balance slowly shifted and I only experienced the occasional bad day. I started to feel able to relax and spend time alone without panicking, and after consultation with my GP, I gradually reduced and then stopped the medication. My concentration and sense of well-being slowly improved and I returned to 'normal'.

My GP suggested that reflection and retrospection would help me to avoid repeating the experience as I would see the warning signs. The counselling helped me to gain insights into what had happened and why, particularly around family patterns of behaviour, and I started on a long path of examining what my life was about and what it meant.

For the next year or so life began to regain its old pleasures. I got used to being single and started to have relationships. My bachelor life at home improved, and I got a lodger to help me pay the mortgage. Throughout this time, I still had a sense of survival rather than full life, as if I was somehow broken and then mended and would never really be strong again. However, after a while I held my own in some routine conflicts in a couple of relationships and started to regain confidence in myself and my resilience. I took an introductory course in counselling just to see how it worked, and was immediately fascinated, so much so that 15 years later it is how I earn my living.

Looking back at the experience, with the skills I have now, it's easy to analyse what happened. I had a series of losses in rapid succession, which is hard for most folk to deal with. In addition, I had followed some family patterns in my marriage which were familiar but which didn't actually meet my needs. I examined and rejected my marriage in a typical mid-life crisis. Finally, I was not very grown up and didn't really know how to face difficulties.

I fell apart, but I didn't die of it, and I came out of it stronger and wiser. Nowadays when I encounter periods of stress I am acutely aware of my mood and if it is low for long periods, I take steps to relax and say no to things which I can't handle. I still get low moods, and oddly enough they are often around the same time of year as other difficult times in my life, as if my emotions hold anniversaries.

I hated being depressed, but that dark time of my life was the precursor of a time of greater wisdom, happiness, growth, maturity and love than I had ever known; and now, in my mid-50s, life is good and is usually getting better.

The Story of Tony,
Barnstaple, Devon

Depression

I recall I first had treatment for depression back in 1966/67. At the time (I was 25/26) I was living in London and working, on and off, as an actor. I shared a small flat in Chelsea with another actor and his girlfriend… well, some of the time. A lot of the time I was out 'on the road' or in repertory, which meant giving up the flat for a while then returning. I had several girlfriends myself; one I was particularly close to. But I wasn't really committed to any of them. It might be said that I have been promiscuous, sleeping around a lot casually.

The nature of theatre work was, I think, one of the reasons for my depression. In work and out of work with great regularity, which was due to the contract-for-the-job system. Contracts would last for various different times. So this led to a very unsettled life, moving not only jobs but changing cities also quite often. As a result, I would be constantly setting up new relationships then ending them. In particular, the 'constant' London relationships I made were also being persistently broken as well. There is also something manic-depressive about acting on stage (most of the work I did) together with identity and personality manipulation. In a sense actors are being 'manic' in performance, putting a lot of energy into each performance, getting 'high' on adrenalin and when the show is over for the night, they enter, or can enter, a depressive phase as one 'comes down', physically and mentally exhausted. Identity is also being manipulated along with the personality. This is because one 'enters' or 'puts on' a different personality with each character.

I was a slim, young, good-looking, middle-class, ex-public school bloke being asked to play a wide range of characters, at different times, who really had little to do with the 'real me'. In the process the personality is also manipulated and one tries to build characters with different persona attributes. For example, in one job I had to play a murderer, a young noble, a young prince and a witch (Macbeth production). In this latter instance, playing an old female crone (in a mask) might be said to be a major identity and personality switch for a young lad about Chelsea! Of course, we could all be capable of murder, but the murderer in question is a seedy professional hit man, a serial killer. Not really 'me' in the least (then or yet, anyway!). A member of the aristocracy (Scottish) I am not, nor of the nobility. So in that production I had to make constant personality and identity changes, albeit fairly short (the witch was the largest part, the others came and went quickly). So I was moving from 'being myself' into 'alternate identities/personalities' very rapidly. On the manic-depressive levels, 'up-down-up-down-up-down' throughout each evening. Then, at the end of each night, I would have to go down into my 'real self'. What made it worse was that I was often in strange towns (it was a tour round the UK) late in the evening, going 'home' to rather low-level bed and breakfasts by myself.

In repertory theatre the identity switch was multiple. During the day, in rehearsals, actors build one character, in the evenings playing another character and late at night studying up on the first rehearsal character. In between, trying to be oneself. The characters change, in some cases, from week to week, in others from fortnight to fortnight and in others from month to month. All of which, in my analysis, puts a lot of stress on your own personality, identity and mood patterns. And, in my 'real self' I rarely had a regular close relationship with anyone in the strange towns I was temporarily living in. Obviously, these take time to establish. Then, if I did establish one, it was broken when the contract ended and I left the town. In effect, while in repertory theatre I lived, breathed, ate, and slept theatre. Which meant living, breathing, eating, sleeping acting and identity/personality change and the associated manic depression. Days were taken up with it, as were evenings and many hours late in the night. The 'real self' had little time to grow, develop his own identity, enjoy himself etc, or put succinctly, HAVE A LIFE. Indeed, instead of having a real life, I had ersatz lives, of many different characters.

It seems hardly surprising that, almost 50 years later, I still have depressive personality disorder and frequently experience extreme identity conflicts, as one identity cluster (groups of thoughts, attitudes, and interests) fights another group internally. It may well be that there are several false identity clusters oscillating around inside trying to occupy the consciousness, causing confusion and depression as the battles are fought. The 'real self' frequently being submerged by false self-needs, interests and desires.

Anyway, the early treatments for depression didn't go into any great depth as to what the causes may be and the pills didn't have much effect, or the private therapies. I totally 'lost the plot' in 1968 while on tour in the sub-continent of India. This time playing two contrasting characters in two different plays (evenings only), moving every week from city to city, every so often from country to country (Pakistan followed by Nepal followed by India followed by Ceylon followed by India again).

A fucking little shit on the tour turned me on to hashish. I became an addict very quickly. I started having what a shrink would call 'hallucinations' but which, to me, were 'visionary experiences of a spiritual nature'. I was deluded into thinking that 'enlightenment' could be reached by way of many joints and chillums. At the end of the tour, I went back to Nepal and got sucked into a heavy dope scene. When I managed to break away from it, I was insane. My real identity totally lost, a false, messianic, identity dominating my consciousness.

Cutting a long story short, I eventually managed to exit the false identity and came down with a crash. I fell deep into long-term depression. I still, today, suffer from depression. The destruction of my career while on dope, the failure to fully recover my sanity, a failure to get back on my feet economically using other art skills – painting, sculpture, pottery, creative writing. My psychological isolation since my common-law wife died in 1987 – and I have not been able to establish a close relationship with a woman since. The existential state of being on my own, being aware I am disabled, have been there since that India episode, with a cognitive disorder, my thought processes scrambled, and not having the wherewithal to find a clear way out of the overall situation, all contributed to depression or depressive states. Obviously, the very darkest states come and go. When I'm 'down there' thoughts of suicide are frequent. Fortunately, or unfortunately, such episodes don't last long and I fight to keep them at bay.

Some techniques I have used include taking regular does of St John's Wort, which I usually take each day and they seem to protect me from the worst depressive moods. I also regularly take Quiet Life, a natural tranquilizer, which I use to control anxiety states and sometimes to help me sleep.

I have also been prescribed drugs – anti-depressants. I appear to be allergic to these; every time they are recommended, I react badly. For example, I feel worse for taking them and end up stopping taking them. I have never been on a long course of anti-depressants of any kind. This is partly due to the fact that the trigger for my 'insanity' in the '60s was a tab of LSD (overlaid on hash). LSD was a drug introduced to the market by the medical establishment. A lot of people jumped out of windows on it; I went totally off my head. The medical establishment causes almost as much suffering as the cure. Cocaine and heroin are two other examples of its depredations. In those cases millions of people have been adversely affected, disabled and killed. I don't trust the psyche medications of the medical establishment. Unfortunately, at this time, it isn't possible to sue for damages. Otherwise I'd take the health system to court for millions.

I have availed myself of various therapies offered by the health system, as prescribed by my shrink. Group therapy, art therapy, cognitive therapy among them. Also I have had one-to-one therapy when I had some money, Jungian and Freudian and hypnotherapy recently. All I can say about any of them is that they chip away at the disability, knock off some of the rougher edges, but never 'cure' it completely. I get the occasional insight, which can be valuable, as to the structure of my psyche and possible causes. But, I believe I 'burnt away' part of my brain surfaces while on hash and LSD so, fundamentally, the condition is incurable. There is structural damage to the way the brain works, which, in turn, seriously affects the way the mind, psyche, and personality operates.

In my view, depression is a very dark mood or gradations of dark moods. Every human being has a mood spectrum, with depression being the darkest or lowest. It is possible to partly control this spectrum. I work out every day to keep fit. I also notice that, while working out, the mood I am in when I start gradually alters. Presumably, as blood is pumped into the brain, the more oxygen it gets. The fitter I am, theoretically, the more upbeat I am likely to be as far as the mood spectrum is concerned and the less often I really slide into very dark moods.

It is possible to view the workings of the consciousness as 'the internal landscape'. This landscape is made up of various key features: a) thought; b) memory; c) emotions; d) personality makeup; e) moods; f) attitudes; g) the Experiencer. The Experiencer rides through this subjective landscape. 'It' is there when one wakes up in the morning and there when one goes to sleep at night, but the thoughts, moods, emotions, attitudes and so forth come and go during any one day. These are transitory, ephemeral, and pass virtually instantly. So the Experiencer can, in part, detach themselves from the other phenomena, and watch various aspects of themselves as they loom into consciousness and out again. The Experiencer is inside each thought as well as being detached from them, inside each mood, as well as being detached. Consciousness, then, is like a cave, the Experiencer is like a person sitting in the cave, the thoughts, moods, and attitudes are like dancers who dance in front of and around him/her. At the end of each day the dancers leave the cave and the Experiencer sleeps. When he wakes the next day, the dance starts up again. So it goes on from day to day, month to month, year to year until the Experiencer also switches off (dies). It is possible, sometimes, to be completely detached from the passing phenomena in the consciousness. It is also possible to watch the thoughts come and go, likewise moods, attitudes, and emotions. These appear to well up out of the subconscious, triggering conscious actions. But, if they are watched by the Experiencer, action does not have to be triggered. I frequently use this 'mind-set' to control depression, eliminate negative thinking, curb negative emotions. A Buddhist monk would, I suggest, be watching the internal landscape nearly all the time when meditating. They might go from sun-up to sun-down in this state. Though it is, of course, impossible to totally ignore the promptings of the flesh, such as urination and defecation, which also appear or disappear at different times.

I usually indulge in self-programming every day after the first workout. While relaxing I repeat over and over such short sentences as "I have a strong will", "I have a powerful mind", "I have a kind, generous, outgoing personality", "I never get depressed" and so forth. These are conscious messages to the unconscious, since our days are often driven by unconscious messages to the consciousness. Many of these can be negative, unpleasant thoughts or inclinations, and emotions welling up. So by feeding into the unconscious positive attitudes, I hope to re-programme my unconscious. If the depression allows, I keep active, keep busy, don't stop and let myself fall into introspection and self-castigation over the many mistakes of the past.

Objectively Tackling Specific Psychological/ Personal Problems

One of the major annoyances of the several disabilities I suffer from is that they intrude on the cognitive processes; my thinking is frequently akin to a piece of driftwood washed back and forth along a shore. It has no bite to it, no focus. This could be either chemical, psychological, result from the burnt-brain effect of the '60s or is a sub-identity, who doesn't want to make an effort, controlling the thought processes. But it is also a depression manifestation, I believe. So if I do originate any activity solutions to my whole life-drama, I rarely have the push to see them through. Depressing –

I'm in a set of problems I can't find a way out of, because I don't have the ability to work out or through any solutions. A mess of a life, largely because I indulged, for six brief months 47 years ago, in hashish topped with one tab of LSD.

The Story of Fiona, Devon

I was born with depression. It is hereditary in my family as is alcoholism. Don't ever let a doctor tell you depression is not hereditary because I have long said alcoholism runs in the family and it is only recently that scientists have discovered that indeed it is. My father had severe depression and was given Purple Hearts, Mogadom and any other drugs that were discovered. I suspect he was used as a guinea pig by his doctors. My mother had a terrible time with him as did we, but she bore the brunt of it. Unfortunately we then had to suffer her anger and frustration. In shielding us from Dad, Mum then became the scary one.

When I was little, I was such a problem my mother was constantly taking me to the doctors to find out what was wrong with me. The initial diagnosis was either brain damage or autism, and then they decided there was nothing wrong with me and sent my mother packing. My sister spent her entire childhood telling me I was the adopted daughter of a witch. At school I was always different and was, as a consequence, bullied constantly. As a teenager I was convinced I was mad – then I discovered I was actually one of the few sane ones in a mad world. In the '70s I actually cared for the environment and thought global issues were actually far more important than what the Joneses thought or had.

When I moved to London, I no longer felt someone was looking over my shoulder and went completely mad. A great many Irish youngsters do this then the burn-out kicks in. Those of us already suffering from depression become alcoholics and/or reclusive. I made a conscious effort to drink myself to death because of the shame and embarrassment my family would suffer if I committed suicide.

The two occasions I actually started to go through with a suicide attempt, my sister turned up unexpectedly. The first time I was about to run through a closed window on the fourth floor.

I cannot hold down a job. I gain employment, am offered promotion because I can be efficient, then panic because I cannot cope with stress or responsibility and deliberately set out to sabotage my own success. Either that, or I become so stressed I just leave. Men, I either hate them after two weeks or I become completely obsessed and almost become a stalker. Friendships come and go. I find the ones that last a little longer are with people with problems similar to mine. But they all go in the end.

When I went to a doctor, he said "What do you want me to do about it?" He sent me to a consultant who listened to all I had to say, then said "What do you want me to do about it?" It was after this I got rid of everything personal and set about preparing my death. But life and my family got in the way, unfortunately, and after a huge argument with the receptionist at the surgery, I started seeing a woman doctor who proscribed Seroxat. It was great for a time but I have changed beyond all recognition. A boyfriend I had at the time would say in front of friends and work colleagues "take another happy pill" to deliberately humiliate me. I had always self-harmed but never had the nerve to try anything worse simply because of the shame my family would suffer. Now I have a child I am responsible for I would not consider it, but it is always there in my mind – it has been since I was seven when I discovered suicide.

Now I care only about my sister and my son. After a disastrous love affair, I no longer have the ability to love. I have never loved my son but the thing that hurts most is I no longer love my horse, and I loved him more than life itself. He was all I wished for my entire life and worked hard to get him and keep him. Now that part of me is closed.

Films, books and music feed the emotions we are feeling and so-called experts who claim they do not really influence us don't know what they are talking about. When I was in high school, I began reading very dark horror stories until I realised it was completely changing my personality. I found I was no longer going outside unless I had to and I was shutting out the world.

Sufferers of depression talk ceaselessly about themselves and as a consequence people begin to avoid them. What they don't realise is that it annoys us too but we can't seem to help it. It's all part of that desperation. We are desperate all the time and we don't know why, which is why we turn to drugs, alcohol and sex.

The Story of Jane,
Plymouth, Devon

"Steve, can you fit this together? If it is no good or not right, it is because it became so overwhelming that I could not write what may be relevant and useful for your book. I have zero self-belief and when I wrote something it just seemed irrelevant and not good enough. Would you consider me texting some of my thoughts about depression and some poems? Jane."

Below are Jane's thoughts, courageously written and texted to me. I will let you be the judge as to whether her story is relevant and useful.

Where do we look to solve a problem? We look to the beginning and that is where I began...

I have tried to find the reason why I suffer this quietly agonising ailment that is called depression. Nature versus nurture has been my obvious route as to why a normal happy but precocious child should be so suicidal by the time she is eight.

When I was a child I planned my own death. At the time it was my only comfort and I knew that if it all got too much I could end it all. My family was what is described as 'dysfunctional'. My life so far has been full of trauma and loss. My father is a chronic alcoholic but is also a gentle soul. It eventually became too hard for my mother to live with him and they divorced when I was only five. The break-up was never discussed – one day he was there and the next he was gone.

It is said that depression can be a manifestation of suppressed anger or anger turned inwards. I was never able to express my emotions to my mother or my stepfather and this left me feeling stifled and caused me to subconsciously deny my sense of self, leading me to believe I was invalid; nothing I thought, said or did was of any importance or use. So I stopped feeling part of this family and withdrew into myself. It was around this time that I started to plan my death as a way out of my deeply unhappy life. I can recognise my sadness and anger towards my mother who let her husband upset her children and alienate them, making it feel like a 'them and us' situation. So, after losing my dad I now felt I was losing my mum and was powerless against a stepfather who used fear and intimidation as an everyday event to show his authority and power over our lives and feelings.

By the time I was a teenager, many resentments had built up and my sense of injustice was simmering below the surface, unable to verbalise my grievances. I sank into depression; I was in a terrible dark and hopeless place. I slept in school uniform so dressing would not be a bother, praying that I would not wake in the morning. My thinking was getting very extreme; for example, if God would not help me then perhaps the Devil would! Lying in my bed I would talk to the Devil, this was my depression at work.

Eventually, I was taken to see a GP and he confirmed that I had depression and suggested I lose weight! Not very helpful given that the weight gained was a symptom of my depression and I was aware that I had a problem with food and was also showing signs of bulimia. I was lifted by some recognition, at least, but only seeing the outside gave my mum and stepfather another way of blaming me for being overweight. The attitude was "what have you got to be depressed about?"

I have carried this depression through until today and I can only live in hope that one day it will go away and I can lead a normal life, if there is such a thing. One thing is for sure, my search to an end to my journey will not stop until such time as I trully and fully get better.

Epilogue

Having just read the personal accounts of depression and how it has affected the lives of the authors and their families, I hope that you have a better insight into what it must be like to live behind the barrier of depression. However, no matter how eloquent or descriptive the words, nothing but nothing can truly convey what it is to exist with the black dog or be down that dark pit. You can only imagine and wonder what it is like to experience the horror and despair of being locked up inside your own unbalanced mind, alone and scared.

On the other hand, we who have been or are still depressed do not fully appreciate how we are to live with for we are too consumed by our own survival and private battles. Do not blame us for we cannot help ourselves despite our best efforts to do so. We only ask for understanding and compassion but please do not offer us sympathy for this does not help.

When I started to write my account and compile the book, I had no idea of how it would develop and what I would eventually write. Once I started to recall my experiences, feelings and emotions, the words came naturally, almost as if directed by an inner force of divine guidance providing the right words and sequences. Events and occurrences came forth that had been buried deep in the black bag of memories that we all drag around behind us, forever getting heavier. This process of writing has truly been cathartic and it has allowed me to lighten that load, to look at my life and choose to see it differently now. I have mentioned this before in the book but it is worth mentioning again, '*it is not what has happened to us that shapes us but rather how we perceive what has happened to us*'.

Since embarking upon the journey that this book has become, I have changed my life around. I gave up my full-time employment that had become a dead albatross hanging around my neck, constantly weighing me down and reminding me of those dark days. This act itself was a struggle, full of anxiety and angst but eventually with courage and determination this was achieved. I am now self-employed working with my former counsellor, Alan, as a personal and business coach. Some may argue that leaving paid employment and substituting this for the uncertainty of working for oneself was foolhardy and could only add to the pressure and stress of producing an income to support myself and my family. There is some truth in this but in reality I now have the ability to make my own choices about how I work, with whom I work, when I work, and how I live my life in general. These choices have given me freedom and allowed me to live fulfilling my newly found purpose in life, to help others.

How many of you can say that you are living your dream? I certainly am and I relish each day with a real passion that I have never experienced before. I now look forward to the future with excitement and anticipation of a new journey, a new awakening and a new perspective. Depression has given me this.

As for the black dog, it still comes to visit and say hello from time to time and bite me in the bum lest I become complacent. It's almost as if he is reminding me of my past, my journey and my purpose in case I forget. The difference is now that I recognise the onset of depression and I can take positive steps to counter its negative effects, such as refusing to offer resistance and to accept its presence without recrimination or self-guilt. These visitations are becoming less and less and the black clouds are parting allowing in the golden rays of the sun and the promise of a blue sky. This promise gives me hope that recovery is well and truly under way, that the black pit is getting shallower and shallower. I can now see over the edge of the parapet and watch the barrier slowly being dismantled. I no longer feel like an insider as I take the first tentative steps to the outside and experience life in a way that for many years I never thought possible. For those of you who have read this book and are struggling with the challenge of depression, I would offer you hope that it is possible to get better, to take more control over your life and to diminish the power of depression. To those of you who live with someone with the illness I say never give up hope for them and for yourself, never stop believing that they will get well again and step through their barrier and rejoin you again on the outside.

Steve

The Professional's Perspective

Author's Note: *Having completed the book, I asked a close friend, who is a therapist and shaman, to read it and give me their feedback. At this point I had not intended to include this in the book, but when the feedback arrived it felt very appropriate and useful to do so. As you read on, you will see why. The text has been copied directly from their emails to me.*

Your sacred book arrived safe and well and it looks like I will be reading it in small bites. Why small bites? Because Steve, it is already provoking a great deal of emotion in me. I had never really seen myself as a depressed person, ups and downs, yes, but depression, no. But as I read about your fall out with your friends and the effects it had on you, it is triggering deep pain in me. Your words are leading me to the very deep place within myself, the place where there is still distress at losing my friend.

In Shamanic terms, what you describe as having happened to you is called "Soul Loss". For the Shaman, the soul is the seat of our emotions, feelings and sentiments. When the soul is traumatised, in effect we lose our vital essence. Our vital soul energy separates from us in order to survive the experience by escaping from the full impact of the pain. Not having our full "essence" available to us, we become lost in non-ordinary reality and become locked into destructive patterns (as you describe your clinical depression), because we are too weak and powerless to move away. We are in fact "outside of ourselves" (often also separated from our memories of the trauma, as what happened to you) and our search for sacred spiritual connectedness begins so that we may regain soul retrieval.

It is no wonder you found Jennie. You know, in spiritual terms, before a spirit reincarnates, it "chooses" the life, and the people needed to enhance their spiritual growth while on Earth. Perhaps you and Jennie made that contract together while in spirit, for both your life's' journey. You said enough in your book about Jennie to let the reader know how strong she must really be, but also how hard and trying this depression was on her also.

You seem to understand that part of you named the "rescuer". Did you ever notice how ANGRY the rescued one becomes towards you after they had looked to be rescued?

I am very touched by your story, of your pain and your determination. Your life has really been your teacher. This is the story of the Fragmented Self. It sounds as if George had some control over your soul. Did you ever hear that a person can steal or borrow another's soul part? This knowledge has been lost in the West, but still abounds in Indigenous people. It is important to know that no one can take your soul without your consent. If someone has stolen your soul, you have in some sense given it to them or allowed them to have it. If you feel for some reason that someone is tugging at your soul, make a firm decision within yourself that they cannot have it and they will not be able to take it from you. What might you have done that allowed George to steal your soul energy to the point of almost destruction? If you can figure this out then you would protect yourself from this happening ever again, with George or anyone else.

I like Jennie even more, she took a huge risk and it paid off. It is clear that she cared much more about your health than the security of your impressive job, that's true love.

I don't know if I told you that my partner went through a depressed time. He is the kind of person who marries their job. They were in a job about 5 years as manager when there was a take over. Within a short time there were many changes, and they began to struggle with the new procedures (for which they had no training). I told

134

them to ask for training to update their skills, but pride and fear would not allow it. Like Jennie, I saw them falling into a deep dark hole. Then, just as you did, they fell apart one morning unable to cope with the pressure. I said "It's only a job, it's not worth this". At that time, I was just entering into my 4th and final year of my degree, which was full time. They were trying to hold on until I had finished the degree. I said I would defer for a year, but this upset them even further (they felt a failure as a person). Anyway I insisted that we would be alright. They were so desperate that they believed what I said. I suggested they had a complete break from work and go on the dole. In the meantime I suggested they did an Introductory Counselling Course to fill in the time, and if they found they were good at it, then they could go to college when I was finished my degree. They were like a child. They so desperately needed Mummy to tell them what to do. So that was what happened. Doctor diagnosed stress related anxiety, and the dole was our saviour.

They took their year out and completed their Introductory Counselling Course, then went on to do a Professional course, and to-day they are earning their living as a psychotherapist.

Jennie found a way forward (even if you were miffed for a while), then you had a little respite, but still something was still in the pipe-line for you to realize, THAT IS THE MYSTERY OF THE SPIRITUAL JOURNEY.

Chapter 4 is all about what the Shaman calls "Dismemberment". At its deepest level, the dismemberment experience dismantles our old identity. It is a powerful death and rebirth process. Dismemberment comes in many guises, and not always agreeable, and often in sickness or mental dysfunction it is a spiritual "CALL", and often the person suffers for years before their healing comes from within themselves (healer heal thyself). This is a Spiritual Initiation where the person dies from his old identity, and is reborn to a new one. He/she must learn how to heal themselves before going on to heal others.

It is making me remember my journey of Initiation. It was arduous and entailed 3 near death experiences, all involving serious illnesses, hospitalization, and receiving the last rights, but still my spirit refused to give up. These experiences that you and I had are the first step that opens the portals of communication to hidden wisdom. Part of my journey brought me back to Tribal people, it was they who taught me the meaning of my life and they helped me understand my life's mission. This is the true meaning of Enlightenment. However, there are many levels of Enlightenment, and each level expands our consciousness even further. Life is not about suffering, it is about transcending the Ego State, and we do that by Dismemberment, which is a Spiritual Emergence. In Spiritual Emergency people often think they are going mad. However, they are not having a break-down, they are having a break-through, and unfortunately not many psychiatrists understand the Transformation. As a result, there are many people in mental hospitals tonight who should not be there, but rather having guidance by a spiritual director, not a medical doctor.

At the deeper levels of yourself you knew all this, which is why you never committed to suicide, you committed to life. You state:-

"This was the last straw, my credibility, which I had always valued and prided myself with, was shattered and I felt sick in my stomach. There was nothing left; I had become a shadow, anonymous and insignificant".

This was a dissolving of Ego, a surrender. This is the beginning of what is called ECSTACY. You are on the Shaman's Path, which is not a religion (unless you decide to make it one), but a Spiritual Path to Enlightenment. But be warned, it is not at all easy, however it is very rewarding but somewhat lonely. That is why you must undergo isolation before hand; your depression gave you that diploma.

You must always try to understand the predicament. For example, your second break-down, there are teachings to be had at such

136

times. At these moments we are vulnerable. In our vulnerability we allow people to get closer to us, we allow them to reveal themselves to us also. I don't know what you feel you learned through this time, but I know you learned what it is to be loved unconditionally, especially by your children. Where do children learn how to be so accepting of their fragile parents, who are the wise ones? It also reflects what you have done right by your children; after all, they model what they learn.

So you saw the strength in your children and the fear in your father. Confusing, isn't it. Fathers are supposed to be "always at the ready" to defend their young, no matter what age. Three generations, Grandfather, Father, & Son.................Grandfather paralysed by fear seeing his son fragile, so looks for understanding; Father in throws of breakdown looks for understanding from his father; Son is neither paralysed by fear, or seeks to understand......he just IS, he just knows what it is to BE (be supportive, be accepting, be there without knowing the answers). Well, what can you learn from that? Without any doubt Grandfather and Father had more knowledge than the Son, but it was the Son who had the most Wisdom. There is a world of difference between Knowledge & Wisdom.
Knowledge is something we get from experience. Whereas Wisdom is knowing what to do with that knowledge.

You talk about your weakness with Jennie. What I hear is strength. It takes great strength to allow a person see you in such pain and risk rejection. Yet you made the space together where your blessed tears could connect you both after a long time of separation. You went from self to selfless, which was a moment of freedom. When we are tied up with "ourselves" we are slaves to our Ego, when we open ourselves to another, we transcend the Ego (a higher level of consciousness). Freedom is associated with Liberation. When we experience liberation we can tap into our own Divinity....now that's Freedom.

Your beautiful depression has led you on to search for meaning. You are bringing the Scientific and the Spiritual components together in a blessed union, and you have found mentors of each. Alan as counsellor will assist the mind (Scientific search), while Lyn as healer will assist your spirit (Spiritual search).

Your depression is probably the greatest "gift", but hard to really know this at such an early stage in your journey. So what is it that is driving you to search? More to the point, what are you searching for... if you found it, would you know it? This is the greatest adventure of the human heart, and I am delighted that you are sharing it with me in your book.

I am also delighted to hear that you are a "healthy sceptic". I am not a believer in "blind faith". For me faith must always be informed by reason. Faith (for me) is the direct experience of ones spiritual nature, but in order to have conscious understanding of that experience we need our informed reason (mind) to bring it alive in the here and now where it can have an impact on how we choose to live our lives.

Life is not about suffering. However, it is usually our suffering that sends us on our search. Everybody has his own story of pain and sorrow. I too have mine, but it is of a different nature than yours of depression, however, we both know that same pain of longing, craving and restlessness that drives a heart to be inclined to suicide. Consciously, the inner craving of a human heart is the attainment of the Real. This is the ladder for one to ascend towards the Unknown.

We go in search of Wholeness. Have you ever wondered what that means? So if we are not "Whole" already, what is the cause? To be whole (Holy) means we are no longer a non-dual self. The dual self operates from our Lower Nature because we are split between body and spirit. We very much accept ourselves as Human, but do not experience ourselves as Spirit. This duality is at the core of all our suffering and conflict. We then split our world into opposites (pain/pleasure; good/evil; happy/sad; male/female; black/white etc). All this is illusion really. So we feel that tear within ourselves, and we go in search of our true Higher Self in order to bring about integration and become non-dual beings once again (Realization, Freedom and Liberation).

This Journey has been a marathon of the heart for me. However, it has been also been wondrous and glorious. If you continue on the Path, you will not be disappointed, but I warn you, it is impossible to turn back.

You will find that your perception of time & space changes beyond recognition (you already felt that when you were in the energy field of your healer, when 30 minutes felt like 10 minutes (time) and sending energy to the Universe (space). You are beginning to experience different qualities within meditation, you say you can quiet the mind, dismiss the idle and negative self-talk and really focus on the here and now, have visions, see your Guides (grandfather and others). You will be amazed at what yet is to come. But with all this comes responsibility also.

It was really good to plot your recovery, going from accepting you needed help, drug therapy, one-to-one therapy and healing sessions, to group work in Spain on retreat, etc. This would give the reader some good firm direction, and also great hope, because you can hear the changes happening in your words as you write. Your feelings of euphoria (what the Shaman calls Ecstasy) tells of those wonderful moments in time when you are connected to yourself. Before we can connect with another, we must first be able to connect with our own self. You probably find yourself going in and out of this connectedness, but that is usual, with more practice it will become your normal awakened state. Of course, we can be knocked out of that state when we experience another trauma (soul loss), and we then slide down the levels of consciousness into a place that is darker and heavier (Grossness), sometimes we can get back to that higher state spontaneously, but more often than not we can do with some help.

Just you remember, these states are neither good nor bad, they just are. The lighter states (called subtle or casual) are higher levels of consciousness, whereas the darker (gross) are lower level states. Each state has its own shadow side (which can cause a Spiritual Emergence), that is why I always advise anyone doing Spiritual Growth Work to have a Master Teacher. As we go through these levels of consciousness we can go into the shadow, and it can be very difficult if you don't know what is happening, you could think and feel that you are going mad. A good teacher will bring you through safely. A person without a teacher may end up in the Psychiatrist care. This is fine if the psychiatrist knows and recognizes spiritual emergency, because if they don't they may confuse this state with a psychotic episode, and the person may be sectioned. A Shaman enters these states of reference at will in order to access different levels of realities (and there are many). The difference between a Shaman and a schizophrenic is:-

"The schizophrenic drowns in the Mystical Ocean, while the Shaman swims".

You ask a good question:

"Had I manifested the return of depression because of these doubts?"

I don't know why you fell down to that lower level again, could be that your spiritual legs are not yet strong enough to hold you up there, and like a baby on unsteady legs, you fall down again. With practice you will develop a strong ego sense and be able to hold it naturally. However, interestingly enough, we can drag ourselves down with our negative thought processes.

Actually, I have a theory, which may not be your cup of tea, but I don't actually think that people are "Depressed" at all. What I

140

think is that people do something called "depressing", this they do with their own minds by their anxious negative thoughts and this pulls them down to a lower level of consciousness. When I work with people who feel depressed, one of the first thing I do is to listen to the words they use. I then look for the deletions, generalizations and distortions in their linguistic speech patterns. I then interrupt those patterns by challenging them. This breaks their trance state. Language reveals what is going on at the surface structures of the mind. For example, if a client says "My boss doesn't appreciate what I do." I get curious and ask questions in order to know what is happening at the deeper structure of mind for that person (unconscious beliefs, values, decisions etc). From careful questioning the client find their deep seated communication with themselves, and together we challenge the distortions. This is very empowering (as you probably found with Alan's work), and the person stops the ANT's (Anxious Negative Thoughts), thus stops "DEPRESSING", for a while at least, and they begin to feel stronger, more in control of themselves. So you see, I think you are right when you asked your question. Our "Thoughts" are very powerful parcels of energy, we should never underestimate them.

Searching & Dreaming, great title, from this chapter I can see your skills of commitment, excellence, research etc. I can also see that your life so far has been perfect for you. I am sure you must be puzzled by that remark. Just imagine for one minute, if we really do choose the life that will give us what we need to fulfil our life's mission, then why would you choose such a hard affliction, such as depression, to be your teacher?

I admire all that you have done so far in order to make sense of your depression. But you know Honey, you are searching for answers in the wrong place, you won't find the answers OUT THERE, I mean the answers that really, truly matter.

Your life is your greatest teacher. Sit down and go inside yourself (your heart and mind) for the answers. They are all there, waiting for you to open your own mind so that you can get your own answers. They are not out there somewhere, you know that by now. The doctors, psychiatrists and books are always giving you some information, but they can't give you this particular knowledge, because it is spiritual knowledge. You need a good spiritual teacher, perhaps you already have those people around you, check them out.

Continue your line of enquiry, all learning is good learning. However, start asking new and better questions:-
What has my life taught me so far?
Why did I need to have this life experience (depression)?
What gifts has it given me?
What is my life mission?
How will these gifts support my life mission?

Remember, if it is true that we choose our lives and family to grow spiritually, why did your wife and children choose you to be in their life? What would they have learned living with depression? It sounds as if your kids are sensitive young people, could it be that they learned how to have love and empathy from the experience? What about your wife, it must have taught her patience, resourcefulness, tolerance, who know what else.

Your Dreams, they are trying to teach you something. But unfortunately you don't get to sleep well enough to process them properly so that you can learn from them.
Dreams are the language of the soul, but you have to learn how to translate the symbols. When you do this, the dreams will change…I promise you that. We all have our demons. But our demons are not our enemies, they are our allies. You need to learn how to work with them, and use the dreamtime for getting more wisdom.

It was great what Alan did with you (Active Dreaming in Altered State). This is similar to the Shamanic Journey, which can be used for getting answers to all your questions. You need to know your life's mission before your suffering will make real sense.

Regarding the title: Searching & Dreaming. The best way to search for meaning (and answers) is through the facility of our dreamtime. Shamans are masters of using altered states to their fullest capacity. I teach my clients how to access their dream state while holding ordinary states of consciousness. What does that mean?

This is a simple version:
We go through several levels of consciousness every day; they range from Beta waves, Alfa waves, Theta waves to Delta waves, each one operating at a different frequency. During our nightly dreamtime, our soul travels out, usually when in the Delta stage when we are in REM sleep. Unfortunately, we don't remember much of it because we are asleep. We are more familiar with the idea of using REM time for dealing with inner conflict. (By the way, I think you are missing out on a lot of your REM time, so you are not getting to resolve your inner conflict. And God knows, boy, you have a lot of inner conflict. Anyone who does not speak their truth in the moment would have, because that leads to inner turmoil, which leads to anger). I use any means I can to help people get good sleep so that they can process the inner conflict for themselves.

I teach my clients how to access dream-time (Theta State, where brain is intensely focused, relaxed, creative and in restful sleep) while holding Ordinary Reality (Beta state, alert and working fully awake). For example, in this state they may ask "show me why I have this depression". In this state the soul can travel in any direction in order to get the relevant information or answers to the questions. As the soul travels, you will see all that it shows you, and because you are also in a fully awake state (as well as a sleeping state) you will remember everything. This is commonly called the Shamanic Journey. All Healers access Theta States in order to be able to use their techniques of healing (even though they may not know it).

Chapter 8, WOW….the black dog & white dog locked into a fight together in this chapter. These two opposing forces are interconnected and interdependent, giving rise to each other in turn. These natural dualities, our Yin & Yang, are complementary opposites within a greater whole. These two parts are aspects of yourself; normal Vs abnormal; good Vs bad; light Vs dark, etc. Steve, did you ever try and talk to these two aspects of yourself, your Black and White Dogs? I suspect the answer is "NO". In Shamanic work, I would take the person into trance in order for them to speak with each part. You would be amazed what comes out of the subconscious, it is rarely what the person expects. These two parts need integration in order to be whole.

Masks
Oh yes, those social masks.

We Wear the Mask
Why should the world be over-wise,
In counting all our tears and sighs?
Nay let them only see us, while
We wear the Mask.
We wear the Mask that grins and lies,
It hides our cheeks and shades our eyes,—
This debt we pay to human guile;
With torn and bleeding hearts we smile,
And mouth with myriad subtleties.
                                    Paul Laurence Dunbar

Masks play a big role in Native American Spirituality, and I bring this knowledge into workshops. In these workshops I invite people to understand the need for us to wear masks. I get them to talk to each of the masks they are aware of hiding behind, to get knowledge as to why each mask is important to them, when and why they picked them etc. These masks deserve to be honoured as they serve us well. We need to give thanks to them, revere them even.

144

However, each persona has its limitation. I then invite the individuals to think about what would happen if they were to take off all the masks. This is very interesting, what it does to them, perhaps you would like to think about that question yourself, right now. People often get a knot in their stomach at the very idea of doing that. Then I change direction. Having discovered how useful the masks are (they give us courage, put us in a mood etc), I then point out that the masks are illusions, but worst of all, they hide our real persona. If they could take off the mask (even just for the rest of the workshop) WHO would they discover they really are, because the limitation of the mask is that it inhibits the true Higher Self from being in the world. We then journey to our Higher Self, our Real Persona and allow it to show itself, its beauty, its diamond quality of Realness, the Spirit of who we truly are. I then get them to make masks that would represent this part of themselves; you should see how each person bedecks that image and how transforming this is.

You know Steve; it is an amazing thing to witness. People come alive in front of me in a way that they have never seen themselves before. It is so beautiful to witness. So Honey, love your masks, they have served you well. You picked them for a reason, just as you did the clothes you wear, you wear different outfits for different events, each appropriate for the occasion. However, there are times when you take off all your clothes, and you bear your Birthday Suite, these are usually very intimate moments, and they are times when you can feel the most freedom. But remember that although the mask can serve you, it also hides your greatest Persona; imagine who you could become if you let that Higher Self shine, WHO WOULD YOU BE THEN????

Regarding your illness, you talk about the importance of putting everything into perspective. You say: "The question then becomes, if I can change my opinions or perspectives, can I break out from behind the barrier of depression?" This line is pulling at me for some reason. I understand exactly what you mean by it, but I am looking at it from a much deeper level. "Perspective" has many meanings, also the perspective can change from one persons understanding to another's.

Your sentence presupposes that "if you can change your opinions or perspectives, then all will be well". But what if your opinions are correct, or your perspectives are right, then changing them would surely be incorrect? I would be inclined to say forget trying to change your perspectives (by the way, they are probably somebody else's conditioning anyway) and continue doing what you are doing. Concentrate on how to become more alive to yourself, to see the goodness of Life, to step out of the dream of your conditioning and to understand better the predicament of being fully human'. For example, if, and just if, your predicament of life is to become a healer (at any level of working), then "depression" may well be your greatest teacher. If your predicament is right, then you will discard the "depressing" when you have milked all you can learn from "her" (your depression). I think "depression" must be female. Why? Because she is reflective, quiet, deep, relentless etc. What do you think?

Put it another way. Have you ever seen a ballerina's feet? I have and I can assure you that dancing "en pointe" is indeed very hard on the feet (and that's not a load of Bolshoi)! They suffer the indignity of blisters, bunions, bruised toenails etc… ballerinas feet are developed over many years. It is a combination of strength and flexibility that create the dancers feet.

The dance of life:

Three steps forward
Two steps back
Painful
Paradoxical result: *beauty*

Imagine those poor feet, what they endured in order to make dance into something so beautiful for everybody to behold. But imagine if the Ballerina had looked at another girls perfect little toes, and had concentrated on her battered feet, telling herself that she is worthless, not a real woman, etc., etc., then fall into despair, crying out "I must change my perspective, then I will have pretty little toes" . What would you say to her then Steve? You would tell her about the beauty of her "triumphant dancing feet", and remind her of the predicament of what it took to get them there. You would tell her to get down on her knees (I was going to say "and kiss her feet", but on reflection, I don't think that would be possible. Oh…. It might be possible for a ballerina!). Do you get the message of what I am saying?

You mention "Envy". Envy is a big part of Toltec wisdom (Mexican Indians). Metaphorically, envy is seen as a kind of highly contagious dangerous virus. There are six main things that people envy: power, money, beauty, body shape, love and youth. Men seem to envy power and money, while women become obsessed with all of them, especially the other qualities.

Envy can serve a positive purpose as well as a negative one. When you are within the "normal" range of envy, the things you desire act as mirrors, messengers from your heart telling you what your soul most desires. Although envy can be incredibly destructive, it can also tell us what makes us happy, healthy, and loving. At such times it is our job to listen. For example, if you envy a public speaker, perhaps there is a part of your soul that yearns to teach, or speak to a group about what you know. The envy may push you to model yourself on this person and become a public speaker yourself (in time). Pure undiluted feelings like envy become little signposts to the intuitive aspects of our personality. They send messages to the mind, giving us the opportunity to analyse the emotions we are experiencing.

I encourage the person to talk about it (often they would not call it envy, but something else). The envy can show me what is not being fulfilled in the person's life, and I work on that, sort of in a Coaching way. For example, a person may complain about their boss, how they don't deserve to be earning as much as they do, because there useless. I may ask them if they felt they could do the job better, they say "of course". So I might ask them, "So what would stop you for going for a similar position?" They will give me reasons as to why not. Usually this is where I can identify the ENVY, i.e. "I never went to college". The envy is mirroring what is missing in the person. I will examine if there is anything that could be done to rectify their predicament. Very often the envy can be charged to make the person take action to change their situation. It is very interesting to work with.

You say "death is better" and I know what you mean. Dying is easy; it is the living that is difficult. Death has a face. Death work is a big part of Native American training before you earn the right to call yourself a Shaman. Soul Work deals with death and dying, and is a big part of spiritual healing. There are many ways to die, but before one can do certain types of "soul work" (i.e. Psycho-pump) the practitioner must be able to overcome his fear of death, and be able to control the death of his own Ego. The Indians put you through your paces, doing advanced techniques using "Will power". Will power and self-discipline help us to choose our behaviour and reactions, instead of being ruled by them.

I don't know if I said this to you before, but do you know that the Indians have a philosophy about the topic "suicide", it is a philosophy that I had held myself long before I heard it from the Indians. "All death is suicide", so what does this mean?

It means that whenever it is that we die, we have surrendered to it. Yes, I hear you say, "But what about those who get killed in a car crash, or those who die screaming". It is the Spirit that chooses it's time to go back to its spiritual home, not the mind. You found that out yourself, didn't you? How many times did your mind go to the precipice? However, your Spirit continued to choose life. You may have though that I was avoiding the subject of your suicidal thoughts, I wasn't, but I just knew that your Spirit was in charge of you, and did not need my sympathy.

You say, "This newly discovered purpose of mine to help and enlighten others and banish the ill-judged stigma attached to depression is what spurs me on".
Eureka! You found your purpose, your life's mission. Without our "purpose" we are only empty shells, the living dead.

Without your depression you would never have found this wealth of knowledge of the subject that you clearly now have. You would never have met Alan, Grace & Lyn (your teachers). You would probably have never "woken up" without your crisis (spiritual emergency), you would never have gone on this Golden Quest, and written this book (spiritual emergence), you would never have read as widely as you have (that gives you specific tools to do sacred work when it is time), I could go on, but I think you know what I am saying.

"Tame the Black Dog". I am glad you said "Tame" and not "kill". You may need to either:-
1. Tame it,
2. Train it, or
3. Develop it.

You seem to think that your Black Dog is your Shadow Self, please journey with him, because I feel this is not the case, I think you will be pleasantly surprised when you dialogue with him.

Don't look for any other state than the one you are in now; otherwise,
you will set up inner conflict and unconscious resistance.
Forgive
yourself for not being at peace. The moment you completely accept

149

your non-peace, your non-peace becomes transmuted into peace.
Anything you accept fully will get you there, will take you into peace.
This is the miracle of surrender.

(Eckhart Tolle)

You say, "Too many changes, too soon and together create a sense of confusion in my identity and sense of well-being and each un-true value has to be tackled slowly and carefully and after considerable evaluation".

You know Steve, Spirituality means being willing to change moment by moment whatever it is that needs to be changed, and I don't think one can create change without either love or spirit. Acceptance is the ground for change and choicefulness. We have to first accept where things are, or should I say where we are in any given moment, because this "acceptance place" is the fertile ground for whatever changes are to grow. I hear it in your words that you know this place, your book is all about it.

Meaning to existence, well done, you got it! But remember, your demons are not enemies, they are allies. An ally is a power capable of transporting a man beyond the boundaries of himself; that is to say, an ally is a power which allows one to transcend the realm of ordinary reality. Of course one may have to battle with his ally demon from time to time, like Jacob with the Angel, but if he should survive (and survive you did) he will be triumphant.

"I have read that it is not what happens to you that affect you but it is how you interpret what happens to you that affect you".

As a therapist, I can tell you that it does not seem to matter if the story of the client is correct or not, what matters is how he/she internalized the event, and the feeling that are left behind. As healers, it is more important for us to stay with the process than the story, and examine the deletions, generalizations and distortions associated with their story. For example, when a woman comes to you with relationship problems, and tells you that she had been raped earlier in her life, of course it is tragic, but your sympathy alone is not going to help her to heal. Then in the course of working together you discover she thinks that "all men are bastards". How do you think this would affect her behaviour with her lovers? Very badly I would expect. It was a terrible thing that happened to her, there's no denying that, but this belief is infecting her present relationships. In effect the abuser is still having a hold over her, she is still a slave to the memory of this incident, and it is making her lonely. She has not forgiven her abuser, not herself for what happened. By the way, in order to forgive one is not required to forget. Actually all of our experiences are our teachers, so why would we want to forget; remembering could save us from repeating painful experiences. Forgiving on the other hand gives us freedom. In her case, free to be open to the fact that there may be at least one man who is not a bastard waiting to give her love. Do you see what I mean?

"I have read somewhere that depression thrives on secrecy and I can see the truth in this". I can also tell you that it is my opinion that "secrets" lie at the bottom of psychosis. Sometimes the secret is so distressing that it actually causes the person to loose their memory of the traumatic event, however the subconscious never forgets anything. This was the work I was doing at the psychiatric hospital... retrieving lost memory. You are right; it is terrible difficulty for people to trust others with their secrets that is why being a therapist/ healer is such a privilege.

To be a "Witness" to anybody's journey is vital to healing. Without a witness, the secrets remained locked in those deep places that cause disruption to the spirit. But this small word witnessing contains the whole of spirituality too.

"Just one quality of the Buddha has to be remembered. He consists only of one quality: witnessing. Witness that you are

not the body. Witness that you are not the mind. Witness that you are only a witness. As the witnessing deepens, you start becoming drunk with the divine. That is what is called ecstasy".

Jennie – The perspective from outside the barrier.

This is a topping chapter, as it gave a well formed indication of the rescuer in the household of the depression. And my word, if they gave medals or badges for 1st class rescuers, then it would be Jennies. It must have been so hard her feeling responsible for your feelings.

Regarding the smoking, while I worked in a psychiatric hospital, I noticed that smoking was desperately important to the patients. So important was it, that it gave the doctors leverage for bargaining. I began to observe the rituals around the smoking. I noticed they would go without food, drugs, visitors, but not their "fags" and this intrigued me. The first thing they wanted after a 5 hour holotropic therapy session was to smoke. I worked out what was happening. In the session huge abreaction took place (discharge of emotions). They wanted to shut off their emotions, and smoking did this very effectively. Each inhale stuffed down their emotions back down, where they did not have to feel them.

Jennie I think when Steve is less frightened of his new found feelings, he will be able to give up the smoking. Perhaps the time is not right just now, as he is only beginning to thaw them out. The more open he becomes, the more able he will be to hold these feelings, he may even begin to enjoy them (even though sometimes painful), and because he will learn so much about himself doing so (that is quite an adventure). When he is ready he will want to do this, not just for himself, but for all of you. I am sure it makes him feel guilty right now hurting you all in this way. Even though the smoking stuffs things down, it takes huge energy to hold them there. So obviously this affects areas such as sexual libido, social anxiety, etc. I know you have some support going on, but do you need counselling for yourself. You may be able to get this free through the one of the

Depression Network Centres. There you may also be able to become part of a group of carers like yourself. It would be good for you to be able to share your story with people who understand your journey, just in the same way it was a relief for Steve to speak to others with depression. You won't be betraying each other by doing this, just getting support for yourselves.

Steve, when you are ready, do not try to give up smoking on your own. Get yourself a Coach who uses hypnosis. Together you will be able to work through not only the physical act of smoking, but also the psychological aspects (which may surface).

Good to hear that you, Jennie, are beginning to treat Steve as NORMAL, yes, that means becoming more real yourself, difficult after being a shadow of your former self for so long. So just take your time to get to know yourself also. It's not all about Steve. Perhaps your mission was to enable him to fulfil his mission (if that is so, then when Steve fulfils his part, so will you, won't that be great?). Go easy with yourself Girl, no need to rush.

The Story of Mark – Falmouth

He says that "Whatever the cause of my depression, trauma, drink, drugs, stress, anxiety, seasons or indeed any combination of these"

"The soul is the life whereby we are joined into the body"
(Saint Augustine)

Saint Augustine was right. We experience all life through our body, whether it is good or bad. And it is the body (along with the Spirit) that has remarkable ways of protecting itself from annihilation

95% of the clients I worked with in the psychiatric hospital were there as a result of sexual abuse. They had been through all the things Mark speaks of before ending up not being able to cope any longer. Regular talking therapy did not work for them either. It was the Holotropic Therapy that went to the heart of their suffering.

Anybody wanting to know more about this subject could read some the work of Stanislav Grof (field of transpersonal psychology). There are many book by him and his wife. "The Search for Self" is a useful book for dealing with "Spiritual Emergency". Grof is a psychiatrist who used LSD with his patients. He found that this brought them to the seat of their pain, where memory was triggered and the client recalled the events of their trauma in depth. However, LSD was banned, and Grof was unable to use it in his work. He traveled to the Amazon where he meet a Shaman who showed him a technique of healing which could do the same thing, it includes using Breathwork and provocative music.

Basically what happens is that when something is so traumatizing that it overwhelms the individual, nature kicks in. It releases endorphins from the brain, which "gates" the experience. This then blocks the system from processing the memory into the long term memory bank. The memory is not lost (as most people think), but rather it lodges itself somewhere in the body (what we call blocks). This energy block can go on to create illness in the body later unless it is released. Holotropic Therapy is one way of unblocking this energy, and when unblocked it also releases the memory with it. This can be difficult for the client, because the memory comes back as if the trauma was happening for the very first time, it is felt with full force.

When in the hospital the whole process of the Holotropic Therapy took about 4 – 5 hours at one time. It took this time to take the person through relaxation techniques, to doing the breathwork (the breathwork brings the person into an altered states and release endorphins, these endorphins are like morphine and relaxes the person). When this happens the body naturally releases the "gates" and the person abreacts (releases the negative emotions associated with the trauma), and the memory of the trauma is allowed to surface. When the person comes back to ordinary conscious awareness we would get them to perhaps do artwork, talk, cry further etc (what was appropriate at that time). A few days later they would have regular psychotherapy in order to integrate the work, and place the event into long term memory bank, where it belongs. We could continue the Holotropic Work every two weeks until the process was worked through. Of course this varied from patient to patient. It was very hard work for both client and therapist, but very successful. The health board did an independent study on our work, and it assessed that it had something like 75% success, that the patients did not continue the "revolving door" process (when they keep coming back into the system for treatment).

The Story of David – Plymouth

By the way, the soul may leave the child who does not feel loved or abandoned by a parent. The soul may also leave to the body to survive sexual abuse. In each of these cases the traumatized person literally escapes to survive the ordeal. David might benefit from some soul retrieval work with a Shamanic Practitioner. It sounds as if he has found his way of Being, for the time being anyway. He is right to trust himself.

The Story of Lorraine - Depression (how it was for me)

Lorraine is a true "Warrior Woman"

Most people think that a "warrior" Indian is a warring man. Nothing could be further than the truth. He fought and killed only when there was no alternative. The primary function of a warrior is a spiritual one; it is in total contrast to that of a soldier. A soldier is a fighting man who acts under orders; he needs to be led, so takes orders from another ranking soldier. A soldier takes no personal responsibility for his actions, whether in victory or defeat. Most people are like "soldiers".

A warrior on the other hand is an individual unit. He is his own "general", and takes full responsibility for his actions. He will do whatever it takes to win and save his people, even if it means retreating for a while, and live to fight another day.

Always the warrior strives to be the best he/she can be, not just have prowess in physical battles, but also in the arts of the psychological, mental and spiritual so that one may have the discipline to change our own behaviour to that of living honourable and in a sacred manner.

The "warrior's" enemies are within the self, and they are unseen. They are the "tyrants" that enslave the mind and the spirit, and keep an individual imprisoned in pain and suffering. Therefore the warrior trains to be proficient not over others, but of him/herself, and the circumstances of their life. The soldier learns how to subdue, whereas the warrior learns how to co-operate. I hear Lorraine has achieved this. She went to battle with her own inner conflict. Going into therapy is to take responsibility for oneself, and to co-operate when being challenged. And she has done that, no easy feat, as you well know.

The warrior is also alive in yours and Alan's story. Did you realize that you were both warriors? From one warrior to another, I pay you homage

I just love this poem below. Does it speak to you at all?

The Gift

The Great Spirit said, "I am going to give you a tremendous gift."
"I hope I am worthy of this gift," I replied.
The Great Spirit said he would inflict me with a disease.
"Disease as a gift?" I asked. I could not fathom illness as a gift.

"What you do with this gift depends on you," he said.
"You can treat it as a curse, or accept it for what it is.

You can lament or make the best of it. It is up to you.
What you do and how you act will prove if you are a Warrior."

He struck me with Polio and paralyzed my legs.
Doctor's said I will never walk again.
But I did. I learned to walk and run.
I thank the Great Spirit every day.
He taught me that those without legs are worthy.

He struck me with Graves' disease.
Life was pure hell for a few years.
Loss of memory, pain, and tremors,
But I got better.

I learned that by helping others with Graves'
I could help to heal myself.
I learned that helping others is a worthy cause.
I learned I had the strength to keep going
Even when I had no strength left.
I learned that as bad off as I felt there was another
Who was worse off than I who I could help.

I learned that instead of reaching for a helping hand
I had become the hand that was reached for.
Instead of being in the abyss I was on the edge
Helping others out of the void.

The Great Spirit said, "I will take your vision."
My eyes bulged and pained.
Vision started to dim and colours were lost.
My eyes went askew and looked in different directions,
But I got better

Sixteen eye surgeries,
Much pain and discomfort,
Orbital Radiation on my eyes left me with cataracts,

But I got better.

I learned that even with no sight I was worthy.
I saw with my mind what my eyes could no longer.
I learned that by helping other's with eye problems.
I helped myself.

I am a Warrior. I no longer look at a person the same.
I see what is inside them, not the shell of the body.
Instead of seeing a person in a wheelchair
I see a person who was given a gift.

I see the Great Spirit gave them a gift too.
I admire their strength.
I admire their courage.
I admire their will.

I pay homage to a fellow Warrior as we pass by.
I thank the Great Spirit for these gifts.
Fore they made me the man I have become.

Lynda's Story - Newquay

This beautiful lady seems to be "dispirited". Without our inherent vitality and connection to the cosmic web, we become disempowered, dejected and **dispirited.** The **shamanic** solution is for the healer to discover why the person is not connected.

Lynda tells us why in her story. When her Father died, she was totally uprooted from her connectedness to her homeland in South Africa. In her psyche, her father was the catalyst to her returning back home sometime in the future. With him gone, there was never a reason to return. So technically, she was uprooted.

Her experience in London never allowed for her to put down new roots. So in effect, she was disconnected from the cosmic web.

She had the insight that it was not a chemical imbalance that she was suffering from, but identified, in her own words, that she felt alienated, both from English people and South African. She is a wise woman to know this.

Because her roots were pulled up from South Africa, and she was unable to re-root herself in London's soil, she could not remember her "way" to any home. This is total disempowering indeed. Without sufficient power we are vulnerable to the environment, therefore quite helpless. This woman has once been a high flyer, but it was at a time when she was rooted to her homeland, and her family.

It seems as if Lynda is beginning to put down her roots in Newquay.......and that is good. I would recommend that if she still feel alienation in the future that she do some Shamanic Healing on her roots. But tell her to wait a while; she may be doing self-healing spontaneously.

The Story of Mrs S – Truro

It is interesting that Mrs. S depression disappeared after the birth of her child.

This was something a professor and I discussed back in the 1990's. I worked with an inmate, a very young woman who accused her family of all kinds of abuse, including sexual abuse. There was something about this young woman that made us wonder about her allegations against her parents. Their behaviour did not fit the usual behaviour of abusive parents, they were always there for her, sad by the situation, but very patient and loving with their daughter, her story did not seem to fit in this case. Anyway, one day we discovered that she had managed to get herself pregnant while on a short release from the hospital. We were worried about her state of mind, but she was adamant that she was going to be a great mother. As the pregnancy advanced, we all noticed her behaviour changed beyond recognition. She became calmer, not the mad hatter she usually was. Where we had to watch her like a hawk because she was into self-harming in a big way, she now began to act very sensibly, and insisted on taking good care of herself. The change was so wonderfully terrible, that the professor and I suspected that her hormones must be playing some part in her recovery. She did keep the baby, and she returned to live with her loving parents (who were delighted with their grandchild). She finally admitted that all she had been saying about her parents were lies. She did not know why she did it, but it was tied up in her getting heaps of attention from everybody. The professor used to laugh at me then. He said he always sent anyone who needed help with their Mother issues to be in my care. The ones who needed mothering would get it in abundance, and the ones who hated and mistrusted women would be challenged by my softness and consistency.

My Experience with Depression – Alan of Plymouth

I was very touched with Alan's story. But out of all the stories, his is the one that demonstrates that there definitely is life after depression. And it demonstrates how one's life story is never an accident, that it leads us, or at least offers us a way to get back on our path when we have made a wrong turning. I know his offering will be a great story of hope for the readers.

DEPRESSION – by Tony of Barnstaple

This man's soul has been searching since he was a young man. He did all the right things to expand his consciousness, unfortunately without his conscious mind having awareness of what it was that he was doing, or to find the right place to do it.

He refers to "consciousness" throughout his essay. This is not a young soul that speaks, but one of the elders. I am not referring to his mature years, I am talking about many re-incarnations, many soul journeys. He is a man who has been struggling to break free

160

for most of his life time. He thinks it is from his depression. I think it is a much deeper yearning.

His career gave him the means of stepping into so many personas, testing, searching, discarding each identity, because it was never the real Self revealed. His craft brought him to his spiritual home (India) where he could have gone to an Ashram where he would have found a Master (or Shaman) of consciousness to work with him, leading him safely up through the levels, while "holding him safely", unfortunately he did not know to do this.

The "Mania" or chaotic *forces he experienced within is such an important part of the Shamans journey to reaching their fullest potential. It is this* "manic state", the state that is highly creative, when often emotionally unresolved people experience as the sharp side of the brilliant Sword of creativity and a highly imaginative Mind.

The drugs, especially the psychotropic trip, blew his mind "upward", and it sounds as if he was hit by a tsunami of a thousand volts of creative and chaotic currents which crashed down upon him, sweeping him out into the Spiritual Ocean, and out to the outer realms of the human mind. This is when a man touches his Divine Energy. When this happens he either drowns, or swims in the fast Ocean. When people see him out there in the ocean, they think he is waving, but Tony was actually drowning. The NHS were never going to recognize what was happening to him, all they know is psychosis, not Spiritual Emergency.

Tony speaks of his experience of using drugs and having a bad trip. Psychedelics are arguably one of the greatest tools for self-exploration known today. Not everyone who wishes to examine themselves needs such a catalyst but for many, if handled correctly, it can be a very useful tool. Psychedelics truly expand consciousness. However, as a person accesses higher levels, they also release the shadow side that resides at those levels. If the person has a Teacher who understands what is happening, they will lead them safely through this rough terrain. However, many people who experiment with these mind altering drugs have no idea of the dangers lurking. And a "bad trip" is likely to push a person over the edge, often creating a psychotic episode, or deeply disturbing the mind. This sounds like what may have happened to Tony.

Fiona's Story

Fiona is right, depression is hereditary, and I will stick my neck out now, and say, not just genetically, but also behaviourally. Not every theorist would agree with me, but then, I am a warrior, I use my own wit in the therapy room, and I study what the client brings in to me (for the good of all).

Many of the clients I have worked with who suffered from depression did not seem to have skills around good survival strategies. How could they. Many had come from a home where there was at least one parent's depression lurked behind every decision, thought and action. How could a child learn good coping strategies in that environment when they are hardly there at all in the home? So instead, the child learns a self-helplessness, which in turn may promote the development of depressive symptoms in the child

It is also my opinion that there is always an "intelligence" at work in all behaviours. Examining and discussing the intelligence of the behaviour with the client is very freeing for the individual. Together we look at what behaviour works or does not work for them to-day. We honour the intelligence of the younger person using these old behaviours (which had worked for them at one time), and then we examine if that behaviour still works for them today. If not, then we explore new strategies of behaviour. I think the human spirit is just amazing, there is no shame attached to the old behaviour; in fact they are honoured by us both. When the person sees for themselves that the old behaviours may be limiting, together we explore more empowering ways. This is very successful indeed.

The human heart longs to be a journeyer, and with help it lusts after the challenge of change.

The Story of Jane – Plymouth

Did you know that children who had a parent who died suddenly have three times the risk of depression than those with two living parents, along with an increased risk for post-traumatic stress disorder (PTSD)

Jane talking to the Devil when nobody else answered sounds logical to me. Poor Lucifer. Everybody hates him, no wonder he has such low self esteem. He had been an Angel, but he dared to buck the system, and he was banished to become a "fallen angel" No wonder Jane turned to him, who else would understand her low self esteem better. Perhaps he needed a friend as much as she did; perhaps he was the one who kept her safe (I wonder did she ever think about that?).

Jane seems to recognise that not only did she lose her beloved father, but also her mother. She was orphaned. This was not addressed while she was a child. How would a child deal with this intolerable situation?

We don't hear how her mother was with the death of her husband. If the mother was grieving, perhaps a bit depressed even (this would not be unusual), this would have stopped the child from being able to grieve herself. Children are known for putting their Mother's pain before theirs, and for protecting the grieving parent. Often they choose not to talk about their own loss because they are worried about burdening the surviving parent. If this was the way it was for Jane, it may have interrupted her from experienced the pain or emotional aspects of the loss of her Dad.

Another normal common response to the death of a parent is to be angry. Jane would have naturally been angry at her father for leaving her, and also mad at God for taking her Dad away, then later her Mum for her betrayal to her. So how could she turn to any of these for comfort? Hence the Devil. How clever was that?

Another thing that is often overlooked is the MANY adjustments to the child's environment over the years, in which a parent is missing. A father is highly important to a girl's development. He is the one the little daughter gets to practice her flirting on. He is so different from Mum (mothers are harder on their girls than their boys), and Dad can be that respite that his little "Princess" needs. He is also the one she can learn to argue with, this is all practice for future male relationships. If Dad can handle her sexuality as she starts to develop, she will feel special, and will look to have special relationships with males later (looking for the re-enactment of the first loving male relationship with Dad). Funny thing, it is Dad that can have a huge impact on the career a girl chooses. Then there are the times when the girl wants Dad just to be there i.e. when she wins her first sporting medal; when she needs someone on her side when Mum is coming down hard on her; when she has her heart broken for the first time (by his rival, may I add), this can be a tough time for both of them, because Dad can't bear to see is Princess hurt by another male. And what about Dad being there to walk her down the aisle and give her away to another male who will, hopefully, love and care for her like her trusted Dad.

Reading between the lines, Jane may have had a lot of changes thrown at her after the loss of her father. It is highly recommended today, that following the loss of a parent it is important (if it can be managed); to NOT move, to NOT change jobs, to NOT put your child in a new school, do NOT get married again. If there are too many changes too soon, it can create too much stress for a child to handle.

Eating disorders are not really about food, they are about "control", or should I say lack of control. Sometimes a child feels so out of control that the only control they can get is by controlling what they

164

put in their mouth, or committing suicide. When I work with eating disorders I am highly unconventional in that I don't mention food. I explore when the client discovered that their pattern of eating was serving a purpose, and what age were they when it begun. I then go back before that time to see what was happening in their lives that was so upsetting. They always go to a time when they felt that life was out of control (it is not unusual to find that there was something very traumatic (i.e. a death in the family, childhood sexual abuse etc). Of course, for many, food is a great comforter; therefore it is common to get anorexia and bulimia as happy campers together.

Regarding "dysfunctional" families, therapists say that 96% of families are dysfunctional, while the other 4% are just liars!!! So Jane is not so different from the rest of us.

Postscript

So we come to the end............or is it really the beginning?

I am glad that your Black Dog still comes around, because you really ought to journey to him. Let him tell you why he is with you all these years, I know you will be surprised when you learn the reasons why. He may not be the one biting you on the bum at all (at least not in a destructive way). I have my suspicions around your White Dog though, maybe he is the one you have underestimated, perhaps your Black Dog is protecting you from some aspects of your White Dog. You need to check this out.

In English folklore, the Black Dog is sinister and malevolent throughout the universe, but sometimes they behave in a benevolent way also (such as the Black Dog of the Hanging Hills and the Gurt Dog in Somerset). In the Celtic Shamanic Tradition the Black Dog was meant to be an omen of death. They have the ability to lead us into worlds we can't see but which they navigate with ease, but before we can accomplish this for ourselves we have to die (metaphorically, from our Ego State, so that we can Transcend that state, and develop our psychic senses in order to enter the Underworld).

Not all cultures see black as evil:-

- Native Americans consider Black to be life-giving soil.
- The Hindu deity Krishna means "the black one".
- The medieval Christian sect, known as the Cathars, viewed black as a colour of perfection.
- The Rastafarian movement sees black as beautiful.

For me Black & White are aspects of our own duality; Yin & yang; good & evil; masculine & feminine, etc. We need to integrate both sides if we are to become non-dual beings. That is the task and role of Spirituality.